Aneroid Barometers
and their Restoration

Cover: *White flash glass 8 inch dial barometer printed with black and red letters in elaborately carved oak case by Negretti & Zambra, c. 1895.*

Also by the author and published by Baros Books:

Care and Restoration of Barometers

Also published by Baros Books:

Antique Barometers: an Illustrated Survey by Edwin Banfield

The Banfield Family Collection of Barometers by Edwin Banfield

Barometer Makers and Retailers 1660–1900 by Edwin Banfield

Barometers: Aneroid and Barographs by Edwin Banfield

Barometers: Stick or Cistern Tube by Edwin Banfield

Barometers: Wheel or Banjo by Edwin Banfield

The History of the Barometer by W. E. Knowles Middleton

The Italian Influence on English Barometers from 1780 by Edwin Banfield

A Treatise on Meteorological Instruments by Negretti & Zambra

Aneroid Barometers and their Restoration

Philip R. Collins

Baros Books

© Philip R. Collins 1998

First published 1998

Baros Books
5 Victoria Road
Trowbridge
Wiltshire BA14 7LH
England

British Library Cataloguing-in-publication Data
A CIP catalogue record for this book is available from the British Library

ISBN 0 948382 11 2

Typeset and illustrations scanned by
Ex Libris Press
1 The Shambles
Bradford on Avon
Wiltshire

Printed and bound in Great Britain by
Cromwell Press
Trowbridge
Wiltshire

Contents

Foreword

While interest in barometers has increased enormously, this has centred in the main around mercury stick or wheel barometers and interest in aneroids has rather lagged behind. Philip Collins challenges this situation by demonstrating, in this book, the wide variety of style and design available in aneroids, as well as setting them in the context of their development both as accurate scientific instruments and as *objets d'art*.

For the would-be collector, the cost of purchasing a mercury barometer is becoming prohibitive. The aneroid, on the other hand, is generally available in much greater number, style and price and is still 'affordable', although early aneroids have increased sufficiently in price. Many interesting later examples are turning up all the time to reward the enthusiast. Aneroids are not just attractive pieces of furniture for the wall, but can also be decorative objects for the desk or mantelpiece, with the added advantage that they are always ready to disclose the likely trend of the weather.

As a maker and restorer of barometers, Philip Collins also offers detailed advice on the restoration of aneroid cases, dials and movements. His enthusiasm and extensive knowledge of barometers of all types are impressive. It is to be hoped that this book achieves its object in stimulating greater interest in the aneroid barometer.

Edwin Banfield

Preface

The aneroid barometer was a revolutionary development in barometer-making in its day, but is presently a rather undervalued instrument compared with its mercurial counterpart. I hope this book will assist in increasing understanding of aneroid barometers and bring a generally greater appreciation of these instruments, both for would-be collectors and also antique dealers who often pass them by as a result of ignorance of their types, dates, and how to restore them.

I have tried to set out the development of the aneroid from its beginnings in 1844. Without doubt, I have wrongly dated some instruments and missed out important ones. I have been astounded in my research to discover that so many different types of aneroid were made: many thousands, and unknown models are turning up all the time. For many months before handing over the manuscript I had to include another 'find' and then yet another!

I apologise for any inaccuracies, but hope that you, as an interested reader and perhaps collector, will help to rediscover Britain's great barometer heritage and inform me of your discoveries. There are areas that will be obvious in the book where information is presently limited and on which I would welcome readers' information. Knowledge has gone with the old craftsmen who made and sold these instruments, and it will be mainly by collection, examination and archive research that our understanding will increase on this absorbing subject – the aneroid barometer.

Important Notice
Chemicals are dangerous, and proper care must be taken whenever handling, storing and using all the materials, chemicals, knives and other hazardous items mentioned in this book.

Acknowledgements

Throughout my career with barometers, which began while working for John Collins & Sons in Bideford, I have met many interesting people who have helped to fire my enthusiasm for these fascinating instruments. They are too many to mention here individually, but I hope they will accept my thanks in general.

My parents are probably responsible for beginning what has become an extraordinary fanaticism with barometers by their gift of a barometer for my 21st birthday. Since then, many other people have encouraged me in my enthusiasm, not least Edwin Banfield who has so kindly loaned me his incredible collection of barometers for display.

Other people have given freely of their time as well as original documents, photographs and other items. I would particularly like to thank John Forster of Barometer Fair, USA, for supplying me with many details and photographs, particularly on the early Dent barometers with which he himself is so fascinated. Thanks are also due to Bert Bolle of Holland for his friendship and courtesy, and for supplying a copy of the Emil Scholz catalogue; the staff of Plymouth Central Library Records Department for bringing dozens of books out of store for me to consult; several private collectors and owners of barometers; Dr Anita McConnell; and the staff of the Science Museum and of the Museum of Scotland.

Finally, my father deserves special thanks for his unstinting work on the illustrations, which has meant hundreds of hours in the darkroom over the past 12 months, because of my inability to grasp the basic points of photography!

Figure 1.1: *Lucien Vidi (1805–1866), inventor of the aneroid barometer.*

1 The Beginning

The word 'aneroid' derives from the Greek meaning 'without liquid'. The advent of an 'aneroid' barometer can clearly be seen as a long-awaited development. Moving glass tubes filled with mercury, or the more transportable mercury barometers designed around boxwood cisterns, must have been fraught with difficulty. In the early years of exploration and discovery, the unfamiliar terrain made travelling hard for the early pioneers. To take a mercury barometer (plus a few spares!) must have been quite harrowing. Even today, you cannot easily send mercury barometers by carrier because of breakages and air bubbles. The invention of the aneroid barometer has been attributed to Nicolas Conté in 1798, but it is thought that he could not make them work satisfactorily. It is, in fact, Lucien Vidi (1805–1866) (Fig. 1.1) who is credited with making the first aneroid 'Vidi Barometer', but, as with so many inventions, it was spurned in its early days as being inferior and of no real use.

Lucien Vidi worked with steam engines, trying to improve them (steam, of course, was a major power then). He thought of replacing the mercury column pressure gauge with a 'corrugated cylinder', but the regulations of the time barred this type of device on a steam gauge. He thought it might be accepted as a barometer, but no one in his native country of France seemed to be interested in the idea. Pierre de Fontainemoreau persuaded Vidi to send his designs to Andrew Pritchard in London. Pritchard appreciated the possibilities of Vidi's ideas and suggested they be made and tested. So in August 1843 Pritchard and Fontainemoreau ascended St Paul's Cathedral and compared Vidi's barometer with a mercury one. They declared the test successful and the first patent was filed on 26th October 1844 by Pierre Armande La Conte de Fontainemoreau (no. 10157). The actual drawings bear little resemblance to what was actually made soon after but embraced the principle of the aneroid, which soon developed into the standard type of barometer used on ships, in the home and in mountaineering. The development of the mechanism is difficult to trace accurately, but, with experience in repairing many, and through the various patents I have discovered, I shall try to place in order some of the developments which I believe to have happened. The best way of dating a barometer is normally from the style of the dial, case and engravings, but it is also helpful to understand various advances in the movements themselves.

Vidi suffered many trials and tribulations in the development of his aneroid barometer. Lesser men would surely have given up. He was engaged in huge law suits only to be disappointed. However, a turning point came when Vidi brought his barometers to Edward Dent (1790–1853) in London. Dent was apparently not well at the time and not at all helpful, but he allowed Vidi to display three barometers in his window. Dispirited, Vidi returned to France, but not for long. A naval officer saw the new barometers and bought them. After testing them he returned to Mr Dent for thirty more! Vidi was near bankruptcy but a friend assisted him and he managed to make more barometers in his own workshop with help from other craftsmen. In 1851 Vidi's barometer was entered into the Great Exhibition in London and was awarded a Council Medal. The aneroid was truly launched. The Vidi Barometer was soon written about and sought after. Vidi's designs were copied in France and England but Vidi failed to get compensation in the courts.

These early Dent barometers are normally numbered on the dial. They generally have the same style of case and similar dials, often with a curved thermometer at the bottom of the dial, usually spirit filled but mercury ones also appear to be original. The movement can readily be recognised from the rear of the case, as the adjusting screw is in a different position from later types (compare with Figs 2.14 and 2.15). Several surviving instruments have the original instruction label on the back, as can be seen in Fig. 1.2, but by far the majority do not have this label. Most barometers were designed for hanging or being contained in a carrying box, or mounted in a box on board ship, but there is at least one surviving example of a later barometer where feet are added so that it could stand on a table or shelf. The dials are not spun as traditional barometer faces but silvered on to flat brass to give a smooth silvered finish. The engraving is quite fine and the movement intriguing. The bellows have been intact on all the ones I

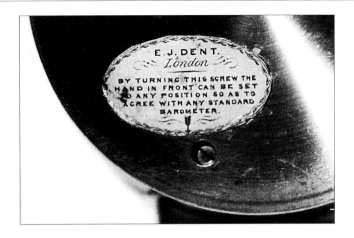

Above, Fig. 1.2: *The back of a Dent barometer showing original instruction label.*

Left, Fig. 1.3: *An oak-cased Dent barometer probably for use on a ship, c. 1850.*

Above, Fig. 1.4: *A typical morocco-covered box, silk lined, housing the precious Dent barometer. This one is no. 541.*

Below, Fig. 1.5: *A bulkhead mounting Dent-style barometer in a metal case with a card dial, c. 1855.*

have handled, and the barometers have been in good working order. John Forster, a fellow enthusiast, informs me that all the ones he has handled, which are quite a number, have always been in working order. This is a considerable accolade for the Dent barometers, as later ones often have damaged bellows and breakages. I can only assume that a high degree of quality manufacture was understood by Vidi more than his successors, and that the copper capsule, which was generally used by Vidi in the Dent barometers, is superior to the materials later used. These brass-cased aneroids were probably supplied in boxes, either polished wood or leather covered, though most are now lost. Fig. 1.3 illustrates an example of an oak-cased barometer which could be secured to a table or shelf. Fig. 1.4 shows a leather-covered case. They were also produced to be fixed on to a ship, as the example in Fig. 1.5 clearly shows.

An important and early work is 'A Few Remarks upon the Construction and Principles of Action of the Aneroid Barometer with Observations on the Mercurial Barometer' by Charles Frodsham, chronometer, watch and clock maker, dated 1849, which adequately describes Vidi's barometer. In fact, it was during Frodsham's experiments on the railway at Brighton that he became convinced of 'the sensitive nature of the aneroid in denoting the transition from one level to another'. This little booklet, possibly one of the earliest descriptions of the aneroid barometer, goes into some detail about temperature compensation and general construction of the barometer. It also includes a chart of trials which were presumably performed just before publication in 1849 and refers specifically to instrument numbers 987, 1013, 1386, 1608 and 1613. This therefore clearly indicates that at least 1613 instruments had been manufactured before 1849. One might assume that one of the most recent barometers would have been used as well, perhaps, as one of the older instruments in these trials. This may not be the case, however, as I have seen details of a barometer by Dent numbered 2818, which was inscribed for presentation 'June 6th, 1849'. If, therefore, instrument no. 1613 had, say, been made in 1848 and the test done and then the book printed in 1849, and if instrument no. 2818 had not been made all that long before being presented, then it is quite possible that a large number of these instruments were made in the late 1840s and that they were selling like 'hot cakes'.

The Science Museum in London has an aneroid barometer by Dent, marked no. 296, which one can assume is a considerably early instrument and therefore probably dates before 1846. The main feature of this early instrument is that it has two thermometers with the bulbs at the '6 o'clock' position, curving to the left and to the right, one alcohol filled and one mercury filled. Many very early Dent barometers do not have a thermometer at all. A single thermometer, however, seems to be the most common. Instrument no. 397, which is probably before 1847, has a slightly different arrangement of wording, having 'M' as the abbreviation for 'Much Rain' and 'S' for 'Set' as in 'Set Fair'. The dial without a thermometer is divided all the way round the circumference in inches of mercury.

There appear to be two distinct manufacturing designs of barometers: the early Dent movements and the later ones. Dating is not easy, although noting a series of manufacturing developments can help. Here are a few clues to look out for:

1 'Paris' is engraved in italic on early movements (this is known from examples up to 3308) and engraved in Roman (upright) lettering at least from no. 3872. Fig. 1.6 shows instrument no. 541 with 'Paris' engraved in italic and Fig. 1.7 shows 'Paris' engraved in ordinary lettering. Dent must have soon realised what a success he had on his hands and, presuming manufacture was carrying on satisfactorily, he must have considered agency sales to satisfy the demand for these instruments. The names of these agents can be found engraved on the dials; for example, Mrs Janet Taylor of the Minories, London, found on instrument no. 2818, dated 1849. An unnumbered barometer is engraved E.M. Clarke, Optician, Agent for the Inventor, 428 The Strand and 19 Exeter Street, London; E.M. Clarke was apparently only at both addresses during the year 1849. How many other agents there were is not clear with so few instruments or details surviving, but there must obviously have been other agents during the late 1840s. By instrument no. 19407 we find no mention of Dent Paris, but a brass Vidi movement with a typical Dent dial is inscribed 'E. Lennie of Edinburgh'. By this time the movement has changed somewhat, which will be discussed later. However, it can clearly be seen that these barometers were distributed fairly widely.

6

Above, Fig. 1.6: *Early Dent barometer no. 541 with 'Paris' in italic.*

Below, Fig. 1.7: *Later Dent barometer no. 6312 with 'Paris' in normal text.*

Fig. 1.8: *E. J. Dent (1790–1853), maker and retailer of aneroid barometers.*

2 The early movements usually have the mechanism held in by squared nuts (known to be done in this way up to no. 6312) and screwed in with screws (from no. 6898).

3 Dials on early Dent movements are positioned into the brass casing by three pins, the case having the necessary holes for these to be located. On slightly later models, the case has three pins mounted into it and the dial fits over the pins.

In the biography of Lucien Vidi of 1867 by Auguste Laurant, he states that more than five thousand aneroid barometers were sold in England before one hundred were sold in France, and this statement is thought to refer to the period between 1850 and 1852 but cannot be proved. So, while it is feasible to assume that any barometer by Dent with a number less than 5000 would be before 1852, it is also likely that some higher numbers could be earlier than 1852. I have a rather poor Dent barometer, no. 3225, which I think I could date with reasonably good accuracy as before 1850, another barometer, no. 8501, which I would put to be after 1852, and a later barometer no. 20377, probably after 1852. However, since Vidi's patent expired on 27th April 1855, it is pure conjecture that larger serial numbers date increasingly further from 1855 as one cannot be certain whether the effect of innovations by other firms meant that Dent sold fewer barometers or whether his greatly acclaimed barometers reached such fame that demand grew such that he was producing more each year. I have seen an interesting use of a Dent barometer at Flambards in Cornwall, where one of these instruments, in the 23000 range, is mounted inside the hub of a wooden airplane propellor, thought to date from around the time of the First World War. Obviously the barometer was secondhand when fitted into the airplane propellor. I cannot think that no. 23000 would have been produced after 1860. My own view is that the majority of this type of barometer by Dent (Fig. 1.8) or his firm were made before 1855 (he died in 1853). It is unfortunate that more written documentation has not come to light, but I hope in due course that John Forster, to whom I am indebted for much of this information about Dent, will continue his research into Dent barometers and produce a much more detailed reference book on these barometers, which were the forerunners of the aneroid barometer and were much copied and used during the last century.

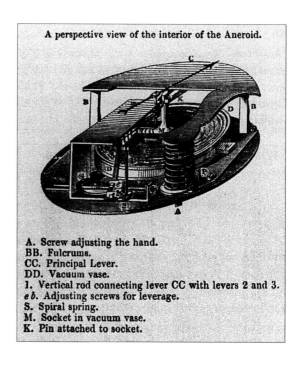

A perspective view of the interior of the Aneroid.

A. Screw adjusting the hand.
BB. Fulcrums.
CC. Principal Lever.
DD. Vacuum vase.
1. Vertical rod connecting lever CC with levers 2 and 3.
e b. Adjusting screws for leverage.
S. Spiral spring.
M. Socket in vacuum vase.
K. Pin attached to socket.

Above, Fig. 2.1: *Perspective view of Vidi movement.*

Below, Fig. 2.2: *Drawing of Vidi movement (top view).*

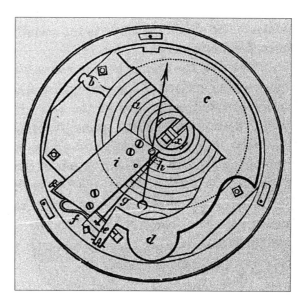

2 Aneroid Movements

The aneroid barometer developed from its early days – through Victorian mass production into the 1930s and to today's modern reproduction and new barometers – via an interesting series of developments which can be split into two distinct types: that of the case and design and that of the mechanism. In this chapter I shall try to put in order some of the developments of the mechanism, from Vidi's first design, with the help of a series of photographs of different mechanisms I have worked on. It is not possible to date these developments accurately: one maker may have developed a new idea or design and yet another maker continued producing in the same fashion. But I believe that there are some interesting variations among the following illustrations which, I hope, readers will, at some stage, recognise in their own barometers. Although I cannot be certain as to actual dates, I believe it is possible to discern a progression of developments, introduced most probably by engineers at the workbench, as much as by any 'inventor'.

Patent no. 10157 (1844) puts on record 'a new mode of constructing barometers and other pneumatic instruments'. Comparing the first drawing of Vidi's patent (Fig. 2.1) with a diagram of an early movement (Fig. 2.2) shows that, like many new inventions, aneroids were quickly modified when put into production. The internal springs of the diaphragm shown in the patent are not apparent in the early surviving Dent barometers and, in fact, the actual parts of the mechanism and hand arrangement are quite different. I have been unable to locate a subsequent patent but the original principle is the same, using a flexible-sided metal box, evacuated of air (the 'diaphragm' also called 'capsule' or 'bellows') to operate a non-liquid barometer.

Fig. 2.3, the mechanism of one of the first of the Dent 4.5 inch diameter barometers, shows an intriguing arrangement of brass levers to transmit the small movement of the diaphragm to the hand. There is almost a transmission box-looking affair with square-headed bolts

11

Above, Fig. 2.3: *Early Vidi movement, 1844–1850.*

Below, Fig. 2.4: *Dent barometer movement no. 397 with dial and bezel removed, c.1845.*

that could be adjusted to allow for calibration. The main arm is rested on fixed pillars and the spring tension is provided by a coiled spring at the bottom of the arm. The patch on this arm is actually an old repair: quite likely the casting was cracked and has been riveted and repaired with a piece of metal. This is not a normal occurrence and as such shows the cost of castings and the economical nature of manufacturers in Victorian days. A further interesting feature is the way the diaphragm is pulled apart. This is done by a spindle being inserted through the cut-away brass lug on top of the diaphragm and the main arm bracket incorporating a hook affair to lift the diaphragm up. The main base plate is also square with the corners cut off. Fig. 2.4 is instrument no. 397's mechanism (c.1845), actually held on with hexagonal screws. I believe that these were possibly replacements, but if another movement with original-looking hexagonal screws were to be found this would be most interesting. Notice how flattened is the pipe used for extracting the air to create the vacuum in the capsule to ensure no return of air before sealing the end of this tube.

Fig. 2.5 shows an instrument dated for presentation 1849 with a large cut-out section in the principal lever. Fig. 2.6 clearly shows the square nuts usually used for holding earlier instruments, this one numbered 6312, with a square section cut out from the cast principal lever. Fig. 2.7, from instrument no. 10729, shows a slightly modified principal lever with a hole in the centre at the end of the arm in which, I believe, a cup is located which houses the spring. Fig. 2.8 shows a major variation in the mechanism of the Dent barometers. This barometer is numbered 19407 with the dial inscribed 'Lennie' but is otherwise a typical Dent barometer. It is more likely to be after 1855 but probably before 1865. The main difference is that there is a large C-spring as opposed to the coil spring and a different arrangement for transmitting the movement from the vertical rod connecting lever. Fig. 2.9, illustrating the movement from instrument no. 21875, is another early variation of the Vidi movement as sold by Dent, incorporating the C-spring dating from the late 1850s. Fig. 2.10, from instrument no. 22175, shows another device of unusual design, with the fusee chain at right angles to the principal lever arm, probably dating from the late 1850s or early 1860s. Fig. 2.11, from instrument no. 24264, c.1860s, shows the use of a quadrant rack and pinion type movement and a C-spring with the principal lever arm on the left,

Above, Fig. 2.5: *Dent movement dated 1849.*

Below, Fig. 2.6: *Dent movement no. 6312, showing square nuts retaining it in the case.*

Above, Fig. 2.7: *Dent movement no. 10729 with a different principal lever design.*

Below, Fig. 2.8: *Dent-style barometer but inscribed Lennie, no. 19407, c. 1860.*

Above, Fig. 2.9: *Dent movement no. 21875 with C-spring, c. 1858.*

Below, Fig. 2.10: *Dent movement no. 22175 of rare design, c. 1860.*

when viewed from above.

Fig. 2.12 shows a quadrant rack and pinion movement with a very peculiar arrangement of levers and balls. It is difficult to recognise where the necessary spring is, but in fact it is a coil spring housed at the end of the principal lever connecting arm. This particular movement is from an instrument by Ritchie with an enamel dial, with the maker's name Bastet of Paris, probably quite unrelated to the Vidi movements but likely to date from the late 1850s to early 1860s. The variation in the Dent movements illustrated is quite fascinating, although this does not generally begin until no. 19407, which was sold by Lennie of Edinburgh, and probably dates from around the late 1850s or early 1860s. Bearing in mind that Edward Dent died in 1853, after his influence was replaced by new blood in the company the design of mechanisms may well have changed – perhaps they were purchased from manufacturers other than Vidi, since Vidi's patent ran out in 1855. It is nevertheless true to say that Edward Dent was the chief initiator of the aneroid barometer in Britain.

Fig. 2.13 shows a barometer in the style of the Vidi early movement, with a flat main arm, supported on pillars, the capsule being lifted apart under tension from a coil spring with a tongue inserted under a pin. However, the lever assembly has considerable modification with a fusee chain and hair spring.

On examining a brass-cased aneroid barometer, the reverse of the case will often indicate what type of movement it is, although there are other factors to consider from the front. Fig. 2.14 shows a Dent barometer case with an adjusting screw that goes up through the coiled spring and is approximately at the '7 o'clock' position, whereas Fig. 2.15 shows a later aneroid mechanism with a C-spring type movement and the adjusting screw is approximately at the '4 o'clock' position. There are one or two slight variations which you may come across, but this is a good general rule of thumb.

Fig. 2.16 is an example of a good-quality Victorian mechanism, c.1860. The capsule is now pulled apart by a C-spring, but still utilising a central clip affair to locate into the top spindle of the capsule. The fusee chain and hair spring assembly is of good-quality brass and on the left-hand side of the lever arrangement, and the main arm is a heavy cast-iron fixing, which has adjusting screws underneath. The knurled brass screw shown at the bottom of the mechanism gives

17

Above, Fig. 2.11: *Dent movement no. 24264 with quadrant rack, c. 1860.*

Below, Fig. 2.12: *Unusual movement by Bastet of Paris, c. 1860.*

calibration adjustment. This movement is from a barometer with a 10 inch engraved silver dial by Samuel and Benjamin Solomons of 39 Albemarle Street, London (1839–1879). Comparing Fig. 2.17 with Fig. 2.16, notice that the adjusting knurled nut is between the lever assembly and the capsule, thus the brass connecting arm is longer and operates at the other end of the axle. This is a very similar design and is still an early aneroid movement.

Early Dent movements are particularly recognisable by the two square-headed bolts that are used for making adjustments to the calibration of the aneroid. Fig. 2.18 shows a Victorian mechanism that still retains this early Dent design. Note also the square-headed screws on the main lever arm. This movement dates from around 1865. Another similar movement is shown in Fig. 2.19, which has the two calibrating screws and the main lever arm retained within two solid brass pivots. This movement probably dates from around 1870. The cast-iron principal lever of Fig. 2.20 is fixed to the base plate with axle slots, V-groove slots in pillars which locate nicely but allow no alteration for tension on the main arm. Interestingly, the arm is on the right-hand side as you look down on the mechanism, as opposed to the usual left-hand side. The spindle assembly arm is inscribed with the number 5250, which is probably the serial number of the instrument, and, being offset, allows further movement of the fusee chain, thus allowing further revolution round the dial, perhaps for a more sensitive instrument or altitude surveying use, the connecting rod not being compensated for temperature. Fig. 2.21 shows a barometer movement, of polished brass and steel, which now incorporates not only the C-spring but also two tension-adjusting screws on the main arm. The axle has a counter-balance and the main C-spring is held by a hook.

The movement shown in Fig. 2.22 is basically of a traditional design, but note the two pillars to hold the hand spindle assembly and fusee chain, the spindle having a helix wheel to allow rotation of hand around the dial of more than one revolution. This invention is similar to the 1886 patent of Henry Samuel Spiller Watkin (see Appendix). Fig. 2.23 is a movement by Watkin. It incorporates the patent no. 14730, a helix wheel for multiple turning of hand, and, instead of the normal hair spring, a fine coiled spring wrapped around the spindle. Note, instead of a lever connection to the axle, the fine fusee chain from the

Above, Fig. 2.13: *Vidi-style movement but probably a copy, not by Dent, c. 1860.*
Below left, Fig. 2.14: *Rear view of Dent barometer, showing position of adjusting screw.*
Below right, Fig. 2.15: *Rear view of later barometer with a C-spring movement, showing position of adjusting screw.*

Above, Fig. 2.16: *Mid-Victorian quality movement (with short arm), c.1860.*

Below, Fig. 2.17: *Mid-Victorian quality movement (with longer arm), c. 1860.*

Above, Fig. 2.18: *Movement retaining two-screw calibration features, c. 1865.*

Below, Fig. 2.19: *Movement still with two-screw calibration feature, c. 1870.*

Above, Fig. 2.20: *Movement showing principal lever held in V slots, c. 1875.*

Below, Fig. 2.21: *Polished movement of high quality, c. 1875.*

Above, Fig. 2.22: *Movement with helix centre, c. 1890.*

Below, Fig. 2.23: *Watkin patent movement with two fusee chains, c. 1886.*

bent connecting arm of the C-spring lever. Again, the main arm is held in position by two stub axles held into the steel base plate. In Fig. 2.24 the movement has the main arm held with triangular pivots on to the base plate, the offset hair spring fusee chain assembly and the now normal cross-pin connection from the diaphragm to the main spring. However, this is now mounted with two diaphragms and the adjusting screw is on the right-hand side of the mechanism as viewed from above, whereas movements of this period usually have the adjusting screw on the left-hand side.

Fig. 2.25 illustrates a very typical design,with the now traditional C-spring and L-shaped main arm with adjusting screw to the left, as viewed from above. It has hair spring and fusee chain assembly of standard design, with the lever connecting axle having a calibration by means of a small screw adjusting the distance of the lever operating the axle. In this instance, the two pillars either side of the axle are of turned brass with pointed screws threaded through to hold the axle. The movement in Fig. 2.26 has its axle with a counter-balanced protrusion but of flat brass, instead of turned brass, the adjustment for calibration being obtained by opening or closing the gap between the axle and the axle lever assembly pin. It is not usual to find the maker's name on the movements of aneroid barometers but occasionally a trade mark or serial number is found. Fig. 2.27 is of another polished Victorian aneroid movement, showing counter-balanced axle, this one inscribed with maker's logo inside a pair of dividers. In Fig. 2.28 the axle is held between two brass pillars with turned brass counter-balance, and calibration is by means of a sliding pin which is held in position by a screw. This is a notable difference in calibration and, in general, I prefer it as you can often make more adjustment than with other types. Fig. 2.29 shows us another variation, being a good-quality movement with turned axle held between brass uprights, adjustable for calibration by knurled nut. Interestingly, instead of a fusee chain, this model utilises a link chain, possibly very late Victorian or early twentieth century.

As time went on, the aneroid movement slowly developed so that it could be made more cheaply, quickly and, therefore, more competitively. Fig. 2.30, while of a traditional design, now has the axle pillars cast in the base plate. The axle uses two pieces of brass, one for the axle and one for the adjusting calibration. It is particularly

Above, Fig. 2.24: *Movement with twin diaphragm, c. 1880.*

Below, Fig. 2.25: *Late Victorian movement, c. 1885.*

Above, Fig. 2.26: *Late Victorian movement with modified axle assembly, c. 1890.*

Below, Fig. 2.27: *Victorian movement in polished brass and blued steel with maker's logo, c. 1895.*

Above, Fig. 2.28: *Late Victorian movement with simple turned axle and sliding pin calibration, c. 1885.*

Below, Fig. 2.29: *Turn of the century movement with chain link not fusee.*

Above, Fig. 2.30: *Movement with axle pillars cast in base plate, c. 1890.*

Below, Fig. 2.31: *Movement with different design cast pillars, c. 1895.*

interesting to see the manufacturer's logo, probably Pastorelli & Rapkin, E5 (possibly relating to model or type). Fig. 2.31 shows another variation of axle pillars cast in the base plate.

As another form of cost-cutting, the axle and the connecting arm were made from flat brass, as in Fig. 2.32, which is probably typical of movements of around 1910. Further finishes also changed as time went on. Fig. 2.33 is probably a movement by Short & Mason in grey painted finish and chromed brass, the connecting rod having a compensation strap. Note the variable connector from the rod arm to the axle to allow for different positioning in manufacture.

All the movements described so far I consider to have been British in design or make, but there were many makers in Europe at the time. Naturally, we see far fewer of these but some are of exceptionally good quality. Fig. 2.34 shows a fine example of one such movement. Note that, instead of a fusee chain, thread is used to connect the lever to the hand spindle. The coil spring, similar to the Vidi, is used to tension the capsule and it has an open fretwork-like bracket or main arm. The calibration design is also similar to the early Vidi movements. It should be remembered here that Vidi fought unsuccessfully to protect his copyright. This barometer movement is a clear copy in many ways of Vidi's own.

One of the biggest changes in aneroid movements since the early designs came as a result of the influence of altimeter designs and improvements, many of them led by Short & Mason. Fig. 2.35 shows a movement incorporating the U-shaped spring instead; there is no bracket arm.The spring curls under the diaphragm and uses itself to support the diaphragm and make adjustments by a screw turning underneath the base plate and pushing on to the spring. This innovation can be identified by patent no. 215844 of 1923, an early design to incorporate this device, and the Short & Mason patent, no. 252887 of 1926. It would therefore not be possible to find movements of this kind prior to these dates. A movement of this design is used in the domestic barometer dated 1946 in its plywood and oak case, shown in Fig. 2.36. The mechanism has a U-shaped spring, only two fixing holes for the mechanism and a shaped or offset axle assembly for transferring the movement to the hair spring spindle.

The movement in Fig. 2.37 follows the Short & Mason patent in utilising the U-shaped spring as the base plate. The assembly is

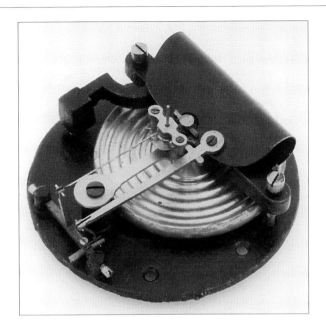

Above, Fig. 2.32: *Movement now with all flat brass axle assembly, c. 1910.*

Below, Fig. 2.33: *Movement probably by Short & Mason with grey painted finish, c. 1920.*

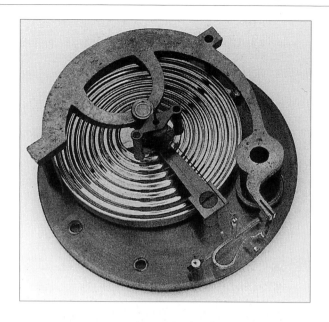

Above, Fig. 2.34: *Continental design aneroid in polished brass, c. 1870.*

Below, Fig. 2.35: *U-shaped spring design movement, c. 1926.*

Opposite above, Fig. 2.36: *U-shaped spring movement in plywood case, c. 1946.*

Opposite below, Fig. 2.37: *Economically designed movement with U-shaped spring, c. 1950.*

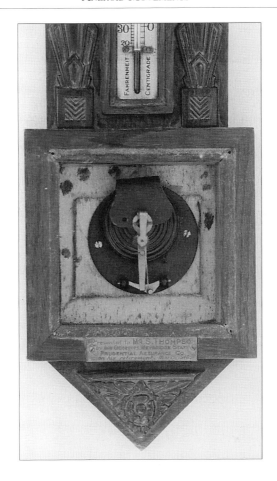

manufactured to more economic tolerances but still maintains the side evacuating lug for the diaphragm which would not normally be expected since patent no. 198838 of 1922 designed new capsules for more accurate calibration by utilising less solder. It is obvious that on many barometers the most up-to-date methods of manufacture were not always used. Some improvements were probably still covered by patent copyright and others were not thought worth incorporating into manufacture of 'domestic' barometers.

Some barometers for the domestic market used extremely good movements and these movements can test exceptionally accurately. The one shown in Fig. 2.38 was probably made by Short & Mason. I have found several that have come via car boot sales and second-hand shops at very low cost but of extreme accuracy, which I presume to have been made just after the Second World War when production was still of a high quality. Of course, not only Britain was gearing up production techniques for altimeters. The German firm, Goerz, made some notable barometers such as the one in Fig. 2.39. The capsule, being self-sprung, tips the lever by a small connecting point, as can be seen in the illustration. This type of mechanism was already in production in 1924, as can be seen from the patent no. 227312 of that year by Goerz. One would not expect to find these movements before 1924, and they are usually associated with the late 1920s and early 1930s . However, I have seen other, much older, barometers, usually French, which have distinctly similar designs to this one.

One advantage of collecting aneroids is the wide selection of old movements still available – the diversity seems to have no end. Fig. 2.40 shows a continental aneroid movement with self-sprung diaphragm, possibly c.1880, which is certainly quite different in appearance. At the other end of the market is the movement shown in Fig. 2.41, which has every appearance of cheap manufacture judging by the very thin metal used to hold it together. Nevertheless, it is a rack and pinion movement which was probably quite good when made, perhaps in the 1970s, and very sensitive. Unfortunately, of the ones I have handled, many appear to have suffered from the diaphragms opening up. It is not really very dissimilar to Fig. 2.42 which is a good-quality rack and pinion movement from about 1890, probably French; these types are often still working. The same sort of movement can be seen in Fig. 2.43 but with a more elaborate fretwork design.

Above, Fig. 2.38: *Rack and pinion movement, c. 1950.*

Below, Fig. 2.39: *German movement from desk barometer by Goerz, c. 1930.*

Above, Fig. 2.40: *Continental movement of unusual design, c. 1880.*

Below, Fig. 2.41: *Rack and pinion movement of cheap manufacture, c. 1970.*

Above, Fig. 2.42: *French rack and pinion movement of heavy quality metal, c. 1890.*

Below, Fig. 2.43: *French rack and pinion movement with fretted design, c. 1890.*

Fig. 2.44 illustrates a good-quality British movement of rack and pinion design from a 1930s style desk barometer. Note the capsules are of side-soldered design as per patent no. 198838 of 1922. Vidi's simple aneroid barometer has at last considerably changed its looks from the earlier pictures in this chapter. If made well, it is more robust, more accurate and more sensitive. British manufacture was still good in the early 1950s as can be seen by the movement in Fig. 2.45, a self-sprung beryllium capsule aneroid barometer movement with aluminium cast mounting and quadrant rack movement; a high-quality instrument, this one was in a very simple case. By 1960, much domestic barometer production in Britain was not orientated to quality. Fig. 2.46 shows a 1960s U-shaped spring aneroid mechanism with cord instead of fusee chain and unusual assembly of hair spring, which makes the whole movement somewhat delicate. This instrument came from a Wedgwood plate design barometer, probably by Short & Mason. The 1970s were not all gloom as far as the quality of barometer movements was concerned. There were still some producers of high quality, as Fig. 2.47 shows. This is a 1970s 4 inch diameter base plate German aneroid movement by Lufft for an oil tanker ship's barometer.

Some barometers can be attributed to particular makers because of the way in which they mounted the barometer or made certain parts. One notable design feature which appears only to be found on barometers by Short & Mason is the sprung dial. Fig. 2.48 shows a wooden case with the movement set in. Around the edge, where the dial will be positioned, is a series of six springs, which are designed to lift the dial firmly up against the bezel and hold everything firm when the bezel is screwed down. This style dates from the 1930s and possibly carried on into the early 1950s. Personally, I find this design unsatisfactory as there is often insufficient clearance between the brass indicating hand and the pressure indicating hand, so that a small misalignment means that one touches the other or the dial. Fig. 2.49 shows another Short & Mason aneroid movement: this one pencilled and probably dated correctly 10th April 1958, housed in a metal case. Note the slots in the rim of the case which are then bent to form springs similar to the above spring arrangement to hold the dial tight against the bezel. Again, this is not a very satisfactory system and one wonders why a more traditional method was not used – no doubt cost came into it. This movement shows rather nicely the

Above, Fig. 2.44: *British rack and pinion movement with side-soldered diaphragm, c. 1930.*

Below, Fig. 2.45: *Rack and pinion movement with self-sprung beryllium copper diaphragm, c. 1950.*

Above, Fig. 2.46: *Small aneroid movement from a Wedgwood plate, c. 1960.*

Below, Fig. 2.47: *German movement by Lufft of still very good quality, c. 1970.*

Opposite above, Fig. 2.48: *Movement in case with springs inset to hold dial against bezel, 1930–50s.*

Opposite below, Fig. 2.49: *Short & Mason movement dated 1958 in pencil.*

additional compensating metal bar added to the connecting rod. The movement is a very fine example of a late mechanism: again, notice the link chain rather than the fusee chain used to transfer the movement from the axle rod to the hair spring spindle.

Pocket Barometer Movements

Aneroid barometers found sudden demand due to their portability and accuracy over the traditional mercury barometer. With increased engineering skills and improvements in design and technique, it is not surprising that the Victorians sought even smaller barometers. In Negretti & Zambra's book *A Treatise on Meteorological Instruments*, first published in 1864, they record that Admiral Fitzroy urged them to reduce the size of the barometer from what it had hitherto been, as well as improving its mechanical arrangement, and compensation for temperature. They accordingly engaged skilful workmen, who, under their directions, and at their expense, by a great amount of labour and experiment, succeeded in reducing its dimensions to two inches in diameter, and an inch and a quarter thick. Compensation was carefully adjusted and the graduations of the dial ascertained under reduced pressure so that they were not quite equal but more accurate, referring generally to mountain barometers and small dial altimeters. They also state that, subsequently, the aneroid was even further reduced in size and was now available from 1.25 inches to 6 inches in diameter and the smallest sizes could be enclosed in watch cases or otherwise adapted to the pocket.

Fig. 2.50 shows an early pocket barometer movement of around 1865, utilising the Vidi-style coil spring to tension the capsule. These movements are often highly engineered, but it was not until later that they could design a small enough C-spring movement. Fig. 2.51 shows a similar movement but with a different hairspring assembly. Fig. 2.52 has improved and now has a compensation strip on the connecting arm. All these movements so far use the coil spring. Fig. 2.53, however, illustrates a pocket movement by J. Hicks from about 1880 which now incorporates the C-spring (of larger movements). The knurled winder allows the user to turn the dial around which is attached to a cogged ring (not shown). Also by J. Hicks is Fig. 2.54, a movement and associated dial dated 1891, with the Watkin patent. This almost certainly refers to the helix centre which allows the hand

Above left, Fig. 2.50: *Early pocket barometer movement with coil spring, c. 1865.*
Above right, Fig. 2.51: *Early pocket movement but with different hairspring assembly, c. 1865.*
Below left, Fig. 2.52: *Early pocket movement with compensation strip. c. 1870.*
Below right, Fig. 2.53: *Slightly later pocket movement with C-spring, c. 1880.*

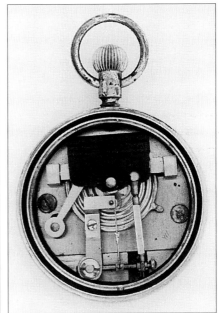

to move more than once around the dial.

Fig. 2.55 is an enlarged picture of a small pocket aneroid movement, possibly around 1880. The helix centre to the spindle can be seen if studied carefully. The screw in the foreground is the adjusting screw for calibrating the instrument by moving the levers forwards or back, whereas previous examples generally show a finely turned knurled nut which adjusts the levers when calibrating in the factory. None of these calibration devices are for the purchaser or owner. Pocket barometer movement design must have followed the larger forms but, possibly because of the difficulty of translating these changes into the small size, these changes followed sometime after the larger movements. This is well illustrated in Fig. 2.56, a 1920s pocket movement with simplified design: this time the hairspring assembly is in the traditional large aneroid form. French manufacturers were also busy making pocket movements, and Fig. 2.57 shows an internally sprung capsule with a quite different mechanism, working on tilting the fretted arm to move the centre spindle. This is probably of French design, circa 1890.

So far I have covered numerous types of aneroid movement, all based on the Vidi-type barometer, generally suitable for the domestic barometer, although some have been from altimeters and early precision barometers. My discussion has been of styles and variations which I have tried to date. There was, of course, a great deal more in the scientific approach to measuring pressure with an aneroid barometer. For the following details on aneroid barometers I am chiefly indebted to C. F. Marvin in a pamphlet (5th edition, reprinted 1919) on *Barometers and the Measurement of Atmospheric Pressure*.

Referring to Fig. 2.58:

> In the common aneroid a lever, *l*, attached directly to the spring connects by a link, *m*, with a very short arm of a sort of bell-crank lever, *r*, *t*, having a horizontal axis on pivots at each end.
>
> The longer arm, *t*, of this bell-crank lever is connected by means of a wire, *s*, with a very fine chain, the other end of which winds around a small wheel or drum on the axis, *a*, upon which is mounted the hand as seen. At *b* is shown a small spiral steel spring, like the hair spring of a watch, which serves to take up the slack in the loose connections of the numerous joints, levers and links.

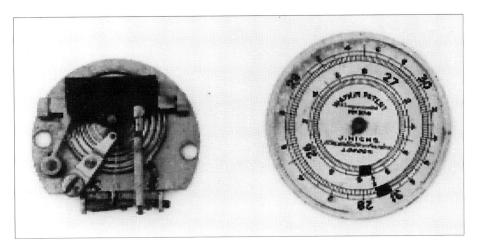

Above, Fig. 2.54: *Watkin patent dial and movement by J. Hicks, dated 1891.*

Below, Fig. 2.55: *Enlarged view of pocket movement with helix centre, c. 1880.*

Above, Fig. 2.56: *Pocket movement with traditional hairspring assembly, c. 1920.*

Below, Fig. 2.57: *Continental pocket movement, c. 1890.*

Opposite above, Fig. 2.58: *Open drawing of aneroid barometer, c. 1890.*

Opposite below, Fig. 2.59: *Goldschmidt's precision aneroid, c. 1900.*

47

At r is shown, also, a small counterpoise weight attached to the bell-crank lever to aid in securing a more stable position of the index when the barometer is placed in different positions; that is, whether the dial is horizontal, or vertical, or turned to one side or the other.

The point of attachment of the link, m, to the bell-crank lever is sometimes adjustable so that the movements of the hand can be made to correspond to the value of the scale graduations.

The steel spring, R, is also slightly adjustable by means of a screw from the underside threaded into the part, N. This permits adjusting the hand to any particular point of the scale to give correct readings.

The steel spring and the feebler elastic reaction of the composition metal of the vacuum chamber are appreciably weakened by increase of temperature, so that in some cases a rise of the pressure may be seen to occur which is really caused by the weakening of the spring. In some cases efforts are made to compensate for this by leaving a small quantity of air in the vacuum chamber, which when heated increases its pressure upward and tends to offset the weakening effect upon the springs. A better plan is to make the lever, l, of two different metals; viz. brass and iron, firmly brazed together. The differential expansion of these two metals with temperature changes produces flexure in the lever. By filing and adjusting the bimetallic bar, the flexure due to temperature can be made very nearly to balance the effect of temperature on the spring. The aneroid is then said to be 'compensated' and this word is often found on the dial. In many cases this word is there when the compensation is very imperfect.

The friction and looseness in the joints of the links and the lack of perfect balance in the various parts give rise to continually changing errors in the reading of the aneroids. This will be shown by tapping the aneroid from different sides and holding it in a variety of positions; a different reading will be given for each condition.

In Fig. 2.59, Goldschmidt's aneroid:

The numerous levers and links in the usual aneroid are dispensed with in this form, and the minute movements of the cell and spring are measured directly by means of a micrometer screw. This is accomplished in several different ways by manufacturers, a common form of instrument being shown here, where the parts have been separated for a better view. The plate, B, with its attached mechanisms, is secured in the bottom of the box, A. The micrometer screw, S', works through the cover of the box. The corrugated aneroid vacuum chamber, M, is held distended in the usual manner by the steel spring, R. A sharp knife-edge projection, a, of a double-formed lever, l, rests upon a smooth polished spot near the outer end of the spring. This spot is sometimes a bit of glass or agate. The lever, l, is pivoted delicately upon an axis at r and is formed of two parts joined near the axis. The upper piece of this lever is a very delicate steel spring, with a flat polished surface at c, which by the springiness of the arm presses against the point of the micrometer screw, S'. At the ends the spring and lever are formed with little flat surfaces, each having a fine line engraved across the middle. This construction is not clearly seen in the drawing. To observe the air pressure the aneroid must be 'set' by bringing the above-mentioned lines into coincidence. For this purpose, and at the same time to measure the movement necessary to bring about such a coincidence, the finely cut micrometer screw, S', is provided. The large head, S, having a scale of graduations engraved upon its outer rim, being turned, the point of the screw presses against the spring at c, deflects it so that the lines upon the ends of the spring and lever may be placed in exact coincidence. To facilitate making this adjustment accurately, a small magnifying glass, L, is generally provided. A small scale is opposite the ends of the lever, l, when the mechanisms are in their normal position and indicates the whole number of turns made by the screw, or, what is the same thing and more convenient, shows the pressure corresponding to the successive positions of the screw. The fractions of a turn are indicated accurately by the graduations on the head of the screw.

The Goldschmidt aneroid is not compensated for temperature, but is generally accompanied by a table of corrections therefore, the temperature being indicated by a small thermometer, the scale of which, in the aneroid shown, is visible through an opening at T.

Aneroids of this pattern are read by first turning the micrometer screw until the lines upon the spring and lever come into exact coincidence. The reading on the scale is noted, and to this is added the part taken from the graduations on the head ...

After being once adjusted to give accurate pressures, as already described, the aneroid should be handled with great care. Violent knocks and shaking will, especially with the usual aneroid, almost certainly change or shift the various links and levers in their joints and change, more or less permanently, the position of the index. For such reasons aneroids are very liable to acquire unknown and often large accidental errors, and can not, therefore, be regarded as very satisfactory instruments.

If an aneroid adjusted to read correctly under ordinary air pressures is placed within the receiver of an air pump, the index will quickly fall to a lower pressure when a partial vacuum is formed. If, however, the vacuum is maintained constantly at the same pressure for many days in succession, the reading of the aneroid will be found gradually to become lower and lower, but after three or four weeks further changes cease or are very small. The amount of this slow change differs greatly and may be from one-half inch or less to over an inch, according to the diminution of pressure and other circumstances. Again, when the barometer is removed from the air pump it does not immediately return to its original correct reading, but its indications will be found to be too low, several weeks being again consumed in a slow return to approximately its former correct reading.

This 'creeping' action depends, no doubt, upon some molecular changes, as yet not clearly understood, that take place within the materials of the aneroid box and steel springs. In any case the readings are liable to be very seriously in error, and tourists and others who carry with them aneroids for the purpose of ascertaining elevations should have means to determine and eliminate the very serious errors referred to above. A further discussion of these errors will be found in the *Monthly Weather Review* for September, 1898, p. 410.

The aneroid barometer is a convenient instrument for showing more or less accurately *the character and the amount of barometric changes* going on from day to day, but the mercurial barometer is the only instrument that gives atmospheric pressure with that degree of precision required in simultaneous meteorological observations.

Aneroids, seemingly good, are often defective, because some of the joints of the levers and pivots are too tight, causing the hand to stick and not move with the perfect freedom it should. The condition of an aneroid can be quickly tested in this respect by tapping the instrument on the side or bottom with the fingers or knuckles, or perhaps better by lifting the instrument about one-fourth of an inch from a table or cane-seated chair and placing it back again somewhat sharply. Under this treatment, if the joints and levers are perfectly free, the hand will jump away and then return quickly with a vibratory movement to its original position. If the instrument is defective, the hand in some cases will not respond to the slight knocks, or will do so without exhibiting any vibratory movement, or upon being disturbed it may move a little, but will not return to its original position.

I do not recommend the test suggested here! A useful simple test if buying at auction is to carry a small plastic bag, place the aneroid in it, blow up the bag somewhat like a balloon and pressurise it. The needle should go up and down as the pressure is enforced and then allowed to lapse. Of course, this is only suitable for pocket and small aneroids, and I cannot see an auctioneer allowing anybody to bring a large plastic bag and put a full-sized aneroid barometer in it. Nor for that matter, rapping it sharply on a table or cane-seated chair!

Above, Fig. 3.1: *Removing hand from spindle with fingers.*

Below, Fig. 3.2: *Removing hand from spindle with small puller.*

3 Restoring Aneroid Barometers

Until recently, it has generally been uneconomic to repair aneroid movements. Even now it will sometimes cost as much as the barometer is worth, but this will change as time goes on and aneroid barometers are thought to be more worth collecting. It is normally an easy task to remove the mechanism from a standard banjo-shaped barometer, after removing the bezel and glass, by unscrewing the retaining screws, the hand being probably the hardest item to remove. Usually this can be pulled off by holding firmly between finger and thumb and lifting straight off the spindle (Fig. 3.1). Sometimes considerable effort is required and care must be taken not to damage the dial which, if card, can easily be scratched. Metal can also be scratched or dented and, of course, porcelain or glass can be cracked. If hard pressure is not enough to move the hand, then a small amount of easing oil may be put into the centre and allowed to work for five to ten minutes. Often this will be even better if left overnight. If this fails, the use of a soldering iron, placing the hot point on the brass arbour of the hand, will usually loosen even the toughest hand. Try heating and letting it cool a few times to loosen it, then lifting as previously described but carefully, of course, so as not to burn your fingers, if still hot.

An extremely useful device can be made by readers skilled in a little engineering, such as that illustrated in Fig. 3.2, which is a miniature version of a hand remover designed for clocks. It has a threaded centre which screws down on to the spindle and a cut-away horseshoe-type affair which clamps on underneath the centre of the hand, and by screwing the top down the hand is pulled up away from the spindle. Fig. 3.2 shows its use on a pocket barometer; of course, two or three different sizes of these tools would be required for the various sizes of hands and spindles that may be encountered.

Once the hand is taken off, the dial can easily be removed by lifting up or unscrewing screws and lifting up. Sometimes nails are bent over the dial; if the dial is glass or porcelain exceptional care must be taken to bend these out of the way before removing the dial. Place all bits aside safely for cleaning and refitting. The use of a suitable box or boxes is very necessary as screws and small parts can easily be lost. The movement should now be visible with its retaining screws (Fig. 3.3). Undo these and the whole mechanism should lift up and out of the wooden case. Occasionally, other designs of fitting the mechanism in, such as holding with nuts and bolts into a metal liner or, indeed, a complete liner soldered to the brass bezel enclosing the dial completely, can be encountered but generally they can be fairly simply removed and there are no particular tricks to look out for. The mechanism shown in Fig. 3.4 needs a new bellows. This can be observed by looking sideways at the movement and the bellows can be seen to have 'blown'. The bellows – also known as the diaphragm or capsule – is shown removed from the movement in Fig. 3.5, which is 'blown' or 'opened up' because air has entered the capsule. A good capsule is shown in Fig. 3.6, where the vacuum is holding the corrugated sides of the capsule tightly together. The mechanism in Fig. 3.5 has been pulled fully apart by the pressure of the C-spring because air has entered the bellows. There can be various causes for this, such as puncturing by accidental falling or inexperienced tinkering, but the most common reason is corrosion or metal fatigue. It should be remembered that the aneroid is constantly reacting to air pressure, and that therefore the movement, although not always regarded, is working 365 days a year; after 100 years it is not surprising that some suffer from metal stress. Today's bellows made of beryllium copper are far more effective and corrosion resistant than most of the earlier ones (if made correctly). It should also be remembered that when the bellows are formed they are stamped out under high pressure into shaped moulds, thus delivering considerable stress to the metal. Although annealed, this process must help to induce stress at a later time. Soldering also includes corrosive fluxes that, if not thoroughly washed, which is nearly impossible inside the capsule, can also create problems. I have repaired several bellows satisfactorily but the percentage of failures is great because of the state of the metal. If a slight hole can be found then the chances are far better.

Fig. 3.7 shows a corroded movement with fusee chain broken, which can often happen when the bellows blow and expand rapidly. This

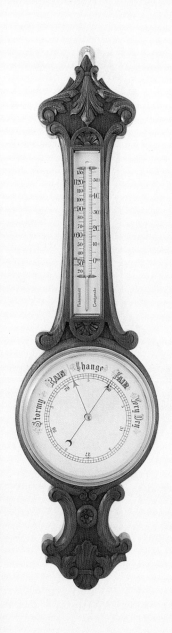 

Left: Ceramic 8 inch dial barometer in thick oak case with carved decoration, c. 1880.

Right: White glass 8 inch dial barometer in a carved case, c. 1910.

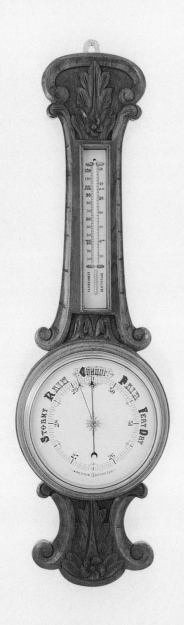

Left: Ceramic 8 inch oak-cased barometer and thermometer of traditional design, c. 1895.

Right: Open white glass 8 inch barometer with simple applied carvings, c. 1930.

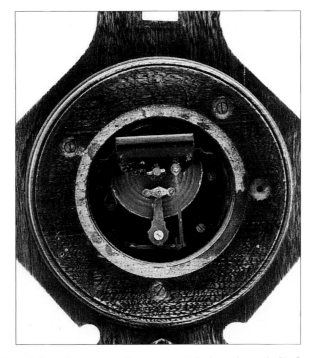

Above, Fig. 3.3: *Movement in case with bezel and dial removed.*

Below , Fig. 3.4: *Side view of movement showing a 'blown' diaphragm.*

Above, Fig. 3.5: *Side view of a blown diaphragm.*

Centre, Fig. 3.6: *Side view of a good diaphragm.*

Bottom, Fig. 3.7: *Badly corroded and dirty movement.*

particular movement was exposed for many years without any glass or dial and has been photographed with dust and dirt intact. The main C-spring is considerably rusty and the brass corroding; the hair spring is screwed up in a ball of twisted wire. Fortunately, few repairs come in quite as bad a state as this. To dismantle the mechanism the use of a special vice is invaluable. It can do in seconds with ease what may take minutes with difficulty without it. The one shown in Fig. 3.8 was specially made so as to be adaptable for different sizes of mechanism and to be held in a vice. Other kinds could be designed, but it is important to hold the spring down firmly to remove the retaining pin. Once removed, the various items can be dismantled for cleaning.

Fig. 3.9 shows the capsule clamping vice in operation. Held in the jaws of a metal vice, a small piece of leather under the main pointed jaw protects the C-spring from scratching and marking, especially when it is a barometer movement that is on open display. With gentle pressure turning of the main screw, sufficient pressure can be exerted on the C-spring to remove the retaining pin. It is important to remove the fusee chain and hair spring spindle assembly (as shown in Fig. 3.9), and to disconnect the end of the main connecting rod, usually by removing the pin in one end or the other of the vertical rod connecting lever. Make a note of which way they are assembled as wrong assembly will mean the needle working in reverse! The brass can be cleaned and lacquered in the usual way, remembering to take care especially to prevent lacquer stopping the free movement of all pivots and so on. When dry, the holes of the spindle and pivots should be checked for free movement. The bellows, if in good order, can normally be lightly wiped over with methylated spirits or thinner and a coat of clear lacquer applied. The steel arm and base plate may just need wiping and lightly oiling if rusting; put a little oil on threaded holes, etc. If particularly rusty, then clean with paint stripper and wire wool and repaint, usually with semi-matt black paint. The main spring often survives and, although replacements are sometimes available, the sizes vary so much that there is no normal size. A good box of parts from scrap movements may be the best solution or else a spring made up especially to suit which, while possible, is quite expensive.

The hair spring can be cleaned if required by soaking in cleanser and rinsing well in a thinner but it is best left alone, if possible, as it

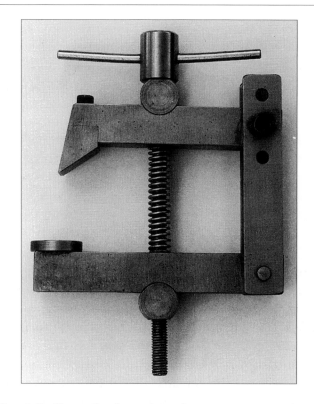

Above, Fig. 3.8: *Capsule clamping vice.*

Below, Fig. 3.9: *Vice in use.*

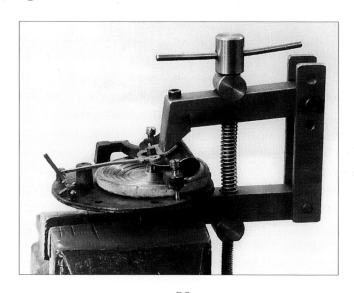

can easily become damaged if slightly corroded. It may well be advisable to replace it with a new one. The fusee chain often becomes sticky and does not coil around the spindle neatly. This will produce incorrect readings. Cleaning in an ultrasonic tank will usually free it up, followed by a very light oil. Broken linkages and fusees can be repaired but require the special skill of a watch repairer who has the necessary tools and steady hands to cope with miniature work. With a good eye-glass and fine tools, one can often make a reasonable job of some repairs but the very small drills required are quite specialised.

Once cleaned and all bits working, the movement can be reassembled. First, fit the hair spring and assemble the spindle and bearing with a fusee chain wrapped around the centre spindle once so as to wind up the hair spring when connected to the appropriate lever. Then fix the bellows in position on the base plate. Do not fully tighten as some movement may be required to allow alignment with the spring. Fix the arm on to the spring and the spring on to the L-shaped bracket by resting the spring assembly on to the base plate over the bellows; with the use of the spring clamping vice, screw the clamp down until there is enough room for the retaining pin to be inserted. Then release the tension slowly (if you have repaired the bellows now is the time to see if the vacuum holds, although often air leaks in again after a few hours, days or even weeks, if not totally resealed). Next position the rocking spindle connector between the two screws and fix lightly. Position the connecting levers into place. New pins or small wire are sometimes required. Try working in a box or tray so that you do not lose any very small parts which are impossible to find once dropped on the floor.

With all assembled, you will now need to calibrate the movement. First, screw the two main screws so that the spring exerts pressure on the bellows. This is normally done by trial and error but there is usually enough tolerance to make adjustments as you proceed. Generally try to position the screws at the same height as before, then screw the adjusting screw to approximately mid-way position. You will quickly see that when the operation range is reached, the vertical lever is moved forwards and back as you screw the adjusting screw up and down. You are trying to set the mechanism so that there is equal movement of the hand up and down to allow for clear movement at different pressures and also allow the barometer to be set at various altitudes and leave enough movement of the hands still to travel up and down the pressure range, 28 inches to 31 inches. To test the movement quickly, carefully press with a finger on the bellows to imitate pressure and lift the main lever arm lightly up to imitate falling pressure. If the bellows have blown then no movement will be detected. When satisfied that the movement is fully assembled correctly, then start calibration. With a test board mounted with a dial (Fig. 3.10), the same divisions as the dial belonging to the movement, screw the mechanism in position. For regular tests a multi-use dial board is useful. Place the board and movement in a pressure chamber, position the indicating hand in the same reading as a test barometer and close the chamber. Switch on the pressure and bring the pressure up to between 31 inches and 31.5 inches and take a reading. Then change to vacuum and bring the pressure down to between 28 inches and 27 inches and check the reading. By comparison with the test barometer, you can normally tell at a glance if the movement is ranged more or less than the master barometer. If adjustment is necessary, remove the board so that you can adjust the fulcrum point and retest.

Fig. 3.11 shows how to make adjustments at the fulcrum to make the hand range more or less. Shortening the fulcrum enlarges the movement, making it longer reduces the movement. Most old 8 inch aneroid dials are ranged on 6 inches of mercury around the dials; that is, there is exactly 6 inches of mercury measured on the dial for $360°$ of travel. Modern aneroids, having more efficient bellows, are usually 4 inches of mercury for $360°$ of travel of the hand (see Fig. 3.12). Old aneroids vary. Early ones often have far less movement than later ones. Sometimes it is not possible even to make adjustment so that the hand moves up and down the same as the test barometer. It will sometimes be possible to make it work on the higher side of change but less on the lower side, and vice versa. Those moving up too much being optimistic, those moving too much to the left being pessimistic! If there is a choice, I would rather have a barometer over-ranged, i.e. moving more than it should, than under-ranged as the whole purpose of weather predicting from a barometer is to follow the trend up and down, not necessarily to measure the pressure exactly.

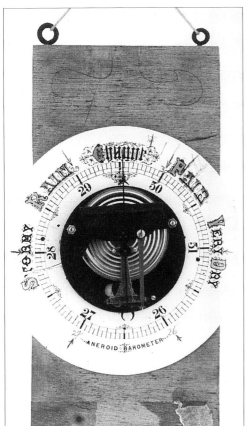

Left, Fig. 3.10: *Movement on test board.*

Below, Fig. 3.11: *Making adjustment to a movement's 'range'.*

Replacement Bellows

If the bellows need to be replaced then there is a selection of different sizes, but, at present, there is none available of the older design, although these may become available as demand grows. Currently available are those made of beryllium copper with soldered flanges (introduced in 1922, see Appendix), such as shown in Fig. 3.13, whereas the older design has a heavier soldered rim at 90° to the convolutions and a solder spigot coming out vertically from the edge (as shown in Fig. 3.6).

Choose a replacement that will fit comfortably within the space where the old one was, choosing slightly smaller if necessary than larger. Take care not to cut the thread at the base as some replacements are evacuated through here. If the thread is too long, then pack the bellows with washers and/or cut a slightly deeper hole in the case, making sure that there is enough room first! On many old barometers, especially oak-cased ones, you will often find a metal liner under the movement. This was put in place to protect the metal-work from corrosion. Oak is very high in tannin and fumes released from the oak when new, even well seasoned, will quickly render the movement useless. After a hundred years, probably less, the oak will have dried sufficiently not to have this problem, although the oak liner does not always work as intended, and some old movements will have suffered considerably from corrosion. The liners are often zinc plated and will usually have a considerable amount of corrosion on them. Although it is best to retain the liner, if possible make sure all loose material is brushed off. If you remove a liner, then it is a good idea to seal the oak inside the barometer around and under the movement with a few coats of thick polish or polyurethane and line with aluminium foil to prevent any further corrosion of the movement from the oak.

Most cases have been packed with three pieces of wood or washers to maintain the correct height of the movement so that the dial does not foul the spring, and the spindle and hand are suitably clear of the glass and dial. With the new bellows, mark the position of the retaining pin to allow the spring to pull the bellows apart sufficiently to become sensitive to air pressure. Allowance needs to be made for the new bellows being thinner than the original one, unless it is packed out with washers when probably the same distance from the base will be sufficient to drill the cross hole for the retaining pin. Old bellows have

Above, Fig. 3.12: *Modern dial with 4 inches of mercury around dial.*

Below, Fig. 3.13: *New capsule with soldered flanges.*

squared holes punched through them so that the pin pivots on the spring. As these are so difficult to produce and the effect is so minimal, a round hole is often satisfactory, re-using the square pin or replacing with a suitable round metal pin. Once drilled, the bellows can be assembled as previously described using the spring clamping vice. It will usually be found that replacement bellows are more reactive than the older ones which will mean trying to adjust the linkage leverage of the mechanism more than was ever intended. If, after testing and adjusting to the maximum, the movement is still too great, then further adjustment of the leverage may be necessary, although to have the barometer working will satisfy most people. To be more sensitive than the original is no bad thing unless it is a scientific barometer or altimeter. To carry out further adjustment than the usual screw allows, it may be necessary to shorten the length of the principal lever. This can be done on some models by simply redrilling another hole closer to the spring and moving the vertical rod closer to the spring, thus making the bellows show less movement.

The brass bar can also be shortened by remaking or adjusting it and it can be bent downwards also to shorten it. However, bending it is not very satisfactory; it stresses the metal too much and means the vertical rod needs shortening as well. If possible, drill and pin the hole and shorten accordingly. On some barometers there are already a series of holes to locate the connecting rods in, which will sometimes be sufficient on old bellows to magnify the movement of less responsive bellows by increasing the leverage. Fig. 2.33 shows a movement where the principal lever has a series of holes in it. These allow for such alterations as have been discussed here without the necessity to drill. I have heard with interest from Mr Appleby of Appleby Scientific how, after the Second World War, tests were done on barometer bellows to see how much air would leak through the very metal itself over a hundred years. Some old bellows will be more porous than new ones but the leakage is not through a hole but atoms virtually going through the metal!

Once the basic principle of the aneroid is understood and a few practice movement repairs are undertaken, it is not much of a step up to using the lessons learned on larger movements to smaller ones. More engineering skills will be needed to make small parts as so many of the brass pieces are not available off the shelf, but, fortunately, they are seldom missing or damaged.

Dials

Card Dials

Many early Victorian dials were printed on card. Be very careful not to wipe these, as often the powdery surface allows the paint to be wiped off very easily. Remove dirt only by very gently brushing with a soft brush or else blow it off.

Enamel Dials

These can usually be safely cleaned with a glass cleaner, methylated spirits or water, but be careful of maker's and retailer's names as these are not usually fired on and will wipe off easily.

Ceramic Dials

If not too crazed, a gentle wipe with a dampened cloth will remove most surface dirt. It can be amazing just how much dirt can build up on old dials – even dead spiders! Be careful of names of retailers and makers as these will have been added after and not fired on generally.

Silver Dials

When shabby looking, they can often be cleaned with a special solution of silver cleaner by sponging or dipping the dial. The silver often revives surprisingly well. Do not use metal polish with any hard rubbing as the silver will often rub off completely. Rinse with water and protect with at least one coat of clear lacquer. If dials require re-silvering this can be done in a similar way to mercury barometer dials and plates. The old silvered finish must be cleaned off, but first check to see whether the dial is printed on, which is the case with some later dials, or whether there is a combination of engraved dial and printed name. In this case, you will need to decide whether to leave the dial as it is or risk cleaning it. Engraved dials can often be recognised by holding up to a good light and looking carefully across the surface at the lines and figures: if engraved, a small amount of sunkenness should be apparent where the wax filling is not perfectly flat; by contrast, printed or hand-lettered names are very slightly proud. The use of a good magnifying glass will be helpful. If you decide to attempt to re-silver then proceed in a similar method as for clock dials.

1 Make sure everything is clean and all materials are to hand.

2 If you require a 'grained' finish (if not go to 4), clean the dial carefully with fine wet and dry paper under clean water or a running tap until all the old silvering is removed. We use down to 1200 grit but experience will tell you how rough to start with, depending on the dial. If in doubt always err on the cautious side.

3 Carefully rub the centre of the dial, while turning it slowly to produce circular rings around the centre spindle hole and then mount on a face plate with a small bolt or screw (bolt preferred as screw may come undone); then, while the dial is rotating, grain the brass dial with perhaps 800 or 400 grit wet and dry paper used dry. Be certain to use a satisfactory face mask to prevent inhaling of dust. When the whole dial is suitably grained, turn off and check in the light if there are any parts missed. On very bad dials, perhaps pitted with age, it may be necessary to leave a small amount: if you continue to clean the dial the engraving may begin to disappear. Once happy with this stage, remove from the face plate and remember not to touch.

4 Should you require a flat finish instead, which is common with pocket watches, you can sometimes achieve this by polishing the surface of the dial with metal polish. Do not use a cloth but find some thick dense cardboard, stick this to a piece of chipboard or MDF board of about 12–18 mm thick and, when dry, cut into one-inch squares. By applying metal polish to the cardboard side and holding the wood (MDF or chipboard), you will find that you can polish the surface of the metal and will be less likely to round off any of the engraving. I have found to my cost that if a cloth is used then the edges of the engraving start to wear away and the wax does not hold in and the engraving begins to spoil. If the dial is deeply engraved, then it may be possible to clean away the first surface with 1200 grade wet and dry paper using water and then remove those marks with cardboard on wood. You may find that a finer grade of metal polish is required and a finer applicator needed. You are actually trying to re-silver an object that was generally electroplated with much more silver than this process uses. Should the wax filling need replacing, this can be done by heating the dial and melting engraving wax into the engraving. The dial will have to be sanded carefully with very fine paper to remove excess wax

so be sure to use fine wet and dry paper and polish out all the scratches. Some very good-quality dials, usually early Victorian ones, have an elaborately engraved centre design which is not wax filled. I know of no way of re-silvering this, as it must have been silvered very soon after engraving and you cannot clean it completely. Fortunately, these centres do not need re-silvering often but remain original when the surface is silvered again. Make sure to rinse any chemicals out of this engraving before lacquering. If the engraving needs to be cleaned, then brush it well out and polish it and possibly wax fill it, which was also done originally, so it will then show up more, and will usually look satisfactory, even if the dial was not originally made like this, although this should only be considered on dials beyond normal re-silvering.

5   Assuming the dial(s) are well cleaned and bone dry, then you should be ready for silvering. The use of gloves is strongly advised. Place a small amount of silvering paste on to the dial and, with a small clean cloth, proceed to rub it well into the entire surface of the dial. You will notice it changing colour and you are aiming to get an even depth of silver deposited all over the dial. After only about 4 or 5 minutes rinse it well under a tap or in a bucket of clean water, and with another small clean cloth rub in some cream of tartar all over the dial. This should immediately start to clean the silver and give it a more even depth of colour. Rinse well and dry quickly with soft tissues then gentle heat. A hair-dryer works well, but if too hot could melt the wax filling.

6   When dried well, apply at least one clear coat of lacquer. Unfortunately, the brand we have been using has been discontinued and others are not quite as good – experiment on a less important piece! Too long a contact with lacquer may melt some wax and a great deal of care and skill is needed. When finally dried the dial is ready to replace on the case.

The above technique is one I find most useful for silvering, but you may well read or discover other ways. Like french polishing, it really depends on which way suits you and gives the best result. The treatment of the thermometer scale is almost the same but it should be grained up and down by hand not on a face plate. A tip that may be useful for mounting round dials on a face plate, or holding thermometer plates secure on a bench while graining, is to use double-sided tape or sticky tabs as they can usually be lifted with a thin blade after graining and can really be useful on small, lightweight items.

Aluminium Dials
These are delicate. Old aluminium is often oxidising after 30 or 40 years if not kept in a good environment, so beware of cleaning: a slightly dampened cloth is possibly all you can do.

White Glass Dials
These are often made with divisions and figures fired on the glass but, again, the maker's or retailer's name sometimes is not. Take care because I have known some dials not to be fired on at all, although they look like it, and a careless wipe can remove the printing on the dial which can be very expensive to put right!

Clear Glass Dials
The lettering, divisions and any patterns are usually printed or fired on the glass in reverse so that the whole movement is visible. A gentle wipe is all that can be recommended as the artwork will also come off if not bonded on to the glass properly or if it has been in a damp environment for some time.

Brass
Clean and re-lacquer if needed but sometimes just a wipe and a fresh coat of clean lacquer is all that is required. Not being very old barometers, the dial is usually in good condition.

Other Materials
Mother of pearl and ivory dials are also possible on aneroids. Take care with anything you are not sure about. One very interesting dial I came across on an old barometer by Chadburns was, in fact, a clear glass dial backed with blue paper with shaped pieces of white glass to make a decoration and the maker's name, letters and divisions marked on the white glass by hand. I have also developed ways of re-making ceramic dials and reprinting transfers to recreate badly damaged white glass, clear glass or ceramic dials, sometimes using the original dial to create the artwork with the help of a scanner, a computer, silk

screen printing methods, a special kiln and lots of time! For that special barometer, it is worth the effort to produce an item not available off the shelf in as good a way as the original.

Case Restoration

Brass Cases

It is very pleasing to find an old brass-cased barometer in original condition and colour, the brass nicely golden in appearance, but this is seldom the case. Generally, brass cases will be worn and dirty, often corroding. It will be a matter of personal choice as to how much cleaning to do, and an evenly oxidised brass case can look very good, like an evenly patinated bronze figure. Gold-plated cases are generally best left intact, perhaps washing any surface dirt away. Re-gilding is expensive and would probably make it look too 'new'. It will also be difficult to get the frosted gold finish so common on Victorian barometers. Silver case barometers can normally be cleaned if required with a proprietary silver cleaner. Brass cases requiring refinishing should be dismantled and then the case cleaned with '0000' very fine wire wool and brass cleaner, buffing on a wheel if necessary but normally with a soft cloth. Sometimes it may be necessary to soak a particularly stubborn case in proprietary horological brass-cleaning solutions. When cleaned and rinsed with cellulose thinner or methylated spirits and thoroughly dried, a clear or slightly coloured lacquer should be applied with a small piece of soft cloth or a very fine brush. To enhance the colour, the brass may sometimes be warmed carefully in an oven, prior to lacquering. Start at about 100°C and watch carefully. Brass, being an alloy, will often colour differently according to its mixture of metals and the size of items being warmed. Even just a soft yellow look will probably enhance the colour but do not forget to watch out for any soldered pieces and, of course, do not include the glass. Great care should always be taken when heating brass.

Wood Cases

The great majority of aneroid barometers were made with wooden cases. Often these survive intact, and generally will only require a careful wax polishing with a soft cloth and brush, before reassembling the instrument, in order to improve its general appearance.

Casework

There are one or two other problems encountered with aneroid cases. A common complaint is the circular wooden ring holding the dial and creating depth in the case to allow the mechanism room for mounting. This circular turned piece of wood is often prone to movement and cracking, as seen on the right-hand side of Fig. 3.14. Fig. 3.15 is a close up view of this damage with the dial and bezel removed. Occasionally, this is of minor difference and can be re-glued, being either a joint opened up or a minor crack. Sometimes, however, there can be excessive twisting and warping of wood and no satisfactory joint can be made without breaking the wood, taking the strain out and re-gluing at a slightly different angle, easing the joint and colouring to suit. Sometimes it is possible to make a series of cuts in the circle of wood so as to take the natural strength out of the wood thereby making it easier to re-glue the crack with sash cramps arranged as in Fig. 3.16, the joint pulled up and glued together carefully. The small G cramp is used to ensure the joint remains level and no step is created or left. As this piece of wood is only a spacer to hold the dial and bezel away from the movement, no strength is needed in it so the radial cuts will not have any detrimental effect on the structure of the carcase. Alternatively or additionally, a screw can be laid in at an angle from the inside to support it further. In extreme cases, a replacement ring may need to be turned on the lathe.

Generally, the majority of banjo barometers from the late Victorian period through to the Second World War were of carved oak cases, being usually from nominal 0.875 inch or 1 inch boards, with carving into the wood, sometimes of heavier proportion, the wood often joined so as to leave one or two inches of wood either side of the dial. These joints can sometimes come to pieces and, if half unglued, can be unsightly. It may be necessary to take apart the joint by carefully easing with a drop or two of methylated spirits or, in stubborn cases, steaming, but great care needs to be taken not to disturb the polish. The joint can be reshot with a plane to make it true without losing too much of the wood, or else the joint will not satisfactorily fit together on the edges, and then re-glued carefully with the use of sash cramps and blocks of wood or cork, so as not to damage the original wood polish.

Missing or damaged carvings can be tricky. These need to be

Above, Fig. 3.14: *Cracked circular mount on edge of barometer case.*

Below, Fig. 3.15: *Close up view of the damage.*

repaired by a competent carver and, when skilfully done, can rarely be noticed. It may not be economically viable in the trade to restore a badly damaged case, but amateurs with plenty of time and patience may well get a very satisfactory finish by cutting away damaged wood, applying pieces of wood of the same type and then re-carving. Frequently, the carvings are matched left and right, so copying is not usually too difficult. Redesigning an entire carving can be a problem when there are no guide lines left, but books and examples of designs may well come in handy.

Thermometer Boxes

Thermometer boxes can also be damaged, particularly the holes in the back (see Fig. 3.17). Although it is possible to cut some of this wood away and let in pieces of pine, by far the most satisfactory repair is to dismantle the box and replace the backing board with another piece of pine, cutting the keyhole slots more accurately and adjusting the screws as needed. Often the thermometer box which is held on with keyhole slots is loose and is a possible source of future breakage; care should, therefore, be taken to make sure these fit well. On slightly worn thermometer boxes it is sometimes a satisfactory remedy to put larger screws in so as to take up the wear. This is probably possible with the thermometer shown in Fig. 3.17. I usually recommend that these boxes are not removed in general use as it exaggerates the wear on them. Originally, they could be taken off and placed somewhere else as a thermometer; this is probably why so many have been lost.

One of the commonest problems on wooden cased barometers in connection with the thermometer box is the moulding which holds the glass in position. Countless times this is missing at the top of the box as can be seen in Fig. 3.18. This piece of wood has often been replaced by a previous 'repairer' who might have used a blunt kitchen knife to shape it from an odd scrap of wood! It is not too difficult a task to measure the thickness of the existing moulding and then prepare from the same type of wood a piece that will match in thickness. Make it wider and longer than needed which will enable you to hold it more easily and have a bit spare if the first piece does not fit well enough. After producing a piece of wood of the required thickness, say 8 inches long and 2 inches wide, use a very fine saw if you have one or else mark with a Stanley knife and rebate a suitable

Above, Fig. 3.16:
The ring removed and clamped together.

Left, Fig. 3.17: *Back of a thermometer box showing 'keyhole' slots to secure on to case.*

Right, Fig. 3.18:
Thermometer box with the top moulding missing.

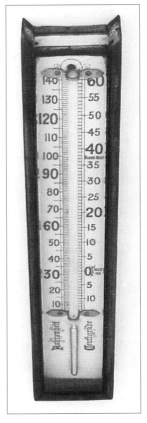

slot to accommodate the glass with a thin chisel. The use of a very fine saw can come in handy for this operation. When a suitable slot has been made in the wood, the trickiest part is to cut the mitre to fit properly. Experience is, of course, the best tool and practice helps. The important thing is for the piece of moulding to be made over size and then the mitres can be trimmed down slowly, either with a sharp Stanley knife (which can be tricky) or preferably with a sharp chisel. To avoid the edges of the slot breaking away, you may prefer to fit a small piece of wood into the slot temporarily so as to hold the edges while cutting. Careful trimming of the mitres and offering up to see if it fits will, given time and patience, result in a good fit. Then you will be able to mark the width required and cut the wood to size, trimming the last few shavings until accurate.

The only operation left now is to shape the top of the moulding: normally this is a simple 'D' or half round shape. This shape can usually be formed with the careful use of a chisel to take the corners off and begin rounding the edge of the wood. A close look and regular trying against the thermometer box will be needed. When close enough, use sand paper to further round the shape: by using a selection of fine grades a good shape will easily be made. Take great care not to round off the mitres while sanding! An alternative approach will be to cut the slot after making the moulding to size. Again, this can be done with a knife and a thin chisel and it may enable you to mark the correct position of the slot from the slots in the side of the thermometer box. When made, an important process is colouring and there is no quick and easy way to get the colour correct. A large selection of stains for different woods is very handy. Some oak barometers will be quite alright with off-the-shelf stains applied a couple of times and, when dry, polishing with a few brush coats of french polish. When dry, finely wire it down and wax polish or treat as the rest of the case. If the moulding you require is of a more complex shape, then you will need to adapt the above methods.

Finishing

With the case satisfactorily repaired, and providing that the polish is reasonable, a very satisfactory finish can be obtained with a gentle wipe with '0000' wire wool or some reviver, such as turps and linseed oil, lightly applied, cleaned off with turps and allowed to dry, or simply by applying a good proprietary wax finish with a brush into the carvings and very carefully polishing back off again. One seldom gets the same problems with mahogany or walnut, although these are less commonly found. When the case is so badly damaged that it needs repolishing, then, with all the fitments removed, it will be necessary to apply a paint stripper to remove the whole finish, but only do this if all other efforts have failed. Not only is it time-consuming, but it is also expensive to repolish and one can never quite achieve the same finish as the old patina on some of these nice barometers. However, when they have been painted or badly repolished with dark varnish, then repolishing is probably the only option. Once the finish is removed with a paint stripper, make sure it has a good clean down with methylated spirits to remove traces of paint stripper. A suitable stain should then be applied and allowed to dry; then, with a very fine-haired brush, apply shellac polish one or two coats at a time, wired down between each one or two coats, and allowing plenty of time to dry in between. To finish, apply a polishing pad on the highlights and flatter areas as best as possible. It is seldom desirable to have an over-polished item and some of the duller shellac finishes certainly maintain a more antique look. The choice of coloured stain will depend on the type of wood and the period of the barometer: this comes with professional experience or customer preference!

Woodworm can be a problem with some barometers, especially oak if there is some sap in it. Excessive woodworm may make the barometer almost worthless but satisfactory treatments, such as proprietary woodworm fluid, should kill woodworm, providing suitable precautions are taken. Another remedy is carefully to place the barometer (case only) in a plastic bag, suck all the air out with a vacuum pump and place in a deep freeze on superfreeze for 24 hours. This will kill all the woodworm inside the case, but great care needs to be taken when defrosting. If the polish is good then some damage can occur. The change in humidity is not good for the wood and this course of action is not recommended unless deemed absolutely necessary. A preferred conservation technique is to have a special fumigation carried out on all infested items. Once the woodworm has been satisfactorily treated, then the small holes can be filled in with a wax stopping of a colour to match the finish of the wood. Always choose a slightly darker colour than the actual colour of the wood, as this will show less. The wax is carefully melted with a warm blunt screwdriver or similar item and the wax pushed into the holes and, when dry, polished off with a soft cloth.

Any damage to the wood surround where the bezel is screwed on, because of the use of multiple screws over the years, should be filled in with wooden pegs and dowels so as not to be noticeable but to enable the bezel to be re-screwed on firmly. Particular attention should be taken on wooden cases, when the movement is being re-screwed into position, that the screws do not go through the back. On some barometers the thickness of wood is minimal and, by over-tightening the screws, the point of the thread can go through the back. If you are at all doubtful, file the end of the screws off; this will often allow sufficient tightening.

Inlaid barometers sometimes require repair. If much inlay is missing this will be expensive, but when there is only a small length of stringing or coloured inlay missing, suitable woods can be cut carefully with a very fine fretsaw using a tracing or rubbing of the shape required stuck on to the wood to be used, perhaps filing with fine needle files so as to fit on intricate pieces. It will often be noticed that the grain on oak barometers is less filled when polished than with rosewood, mahogany and walnut. In general, aneroid wooden cases suffer little damage as they are seldom veneered, unlike their mercury counterparts, and therefore case repairs are often small and waxing covers the majority.

4 Brass-cased and Ship-style barometers

There is often considerable misunderstanding about ship's barometers. Although aneroid barometers were quickly seen to be of great importance for use on board ships and boats, and while early aneroids would certainly soon have been used on board ship, they would have been used in conjunction with a mercury barometer for some while until their dependability was satisfactorily established. New instruments or tools are often shunned at first, perhaps by the more traditional and older members of society. It is quite likely that it took many years before the aneroid barometer was truly accepted for use on board ship without the back-up of the essential mercury barometer. On board ship, the barometer to be hung on a wall would need to be secured safely so any 'ship's barometer' with only one hanging would not be hung in the ship but kept in a case, or, more likely, it would have been made, as they often were, with two or sometimes three fixing brackets so that they would not swing if screwed to the wall of the ship. It is possible that gimballed aneroid barometers were made but I have never come across any. There was no need for them to move within a gimbal and, if they were screwed against the side of the ship, any vibration would automatically adjust the barometer against any friction building up in the movement.

Fig. 4.1 shows a typical 4.5 inch diameter dial Dent barometer, inscribed 'E.J. Dent, Paris, no. 2643' with a Fahrenheit scale thermometer, spirit filled, still in operational condition. Dating from about the late 1840s, the narrow tapered arrowpoint hands are a particular feature of these barometers, with the case in spun brass and the front bezel having a machined patterned knurled effect. Earlier Dent barometers were signed E. J. Dent in script rather than the capital letters that can be seen in the figure. Fig. 4.2 shows a 6 inch dial aneroid barometer with curved mercury-filled thermometer, the dial engraved 'holosteric barometer'. It is French, made for the

English market, no longer by Dent, circa 1860s, with a finely engraved dial with visible movement. The much larger dial shown in Fig. 4.3 is an unsigned 8 inch engraved brass open dial brass-cased barometer, with twin thermometers: Centigrade and Reaumur in alcohol on the left, and Fahrenheit in mercury on the right. Again, this is probably French in origin for the English market, and these barometers were often sold on stands of carved wood, around 1870. An unusual oak-cased ship's barometer is featured in Fig. 4.4 with a 5 inch porcelain dial made for the Shipwrecked Fishermen & Mariners' Royal Benevolent Society by Dollond, circa 1880, with black and red coloured dial. With a much more robost, certainly heavier case, Fig. 4.5 illustrates the Universal Barometer, being a 5 inch painted metal dial in cast-iron housing for 'the use of mariners, agriculturists and horticulturists'. Note the interesting variation in the weather words: 'Stormy', 'Unsettled' and 'Fair Weather'. This was possibly for use outside or in greenhouses and sheds more open to the elements: hence the cast-iron case. Figs 4.6 and 4.7 are so similar that they could have been made by the same manufacturer, but the first is a fisherman's aneroid barometer with a 5 inch enamel dial issued by the Royal National Lifeboat Institution and made by Negretti & Zambra, London, circa 1890, again with red and black lettering in a soft metal casing, with black paint finish. The second is a fisherman's aneroid barometer with 4.75 inch ceramic dial, this one numbered 3641, made by Dollond of London, with red and black letters and numbers, in black painted metal case with brass bezel.

Enamel and ceramic dials were almost certainly made for use at sea but would have cost more. There are still many barometers surviving with card dials and often the earlier ones have very good-quality dials. Although they may not always be in a clean condition, they do not suffer from broken dials and could be more robust for that reason. Fig. 4.8 shows a fine example of a 4.5 inch card dial brass-cased barometer with straight mercury-filled thermometer showing Fahrenheit and Reaumur scales. The dial is in good condition showing fine printed lines, circa late 1860s. Card dials also lent themselves more easily to being named by the retailer, as Fig. 4.9 shows. It is a 4.5 inch carved dial brass-cased barometer in distressed condition, the dial surviving reasonably well with some marks. The name of the retailer, 'Husbands, 8 St Augustine's Parade, Bristol', is hand-lettered

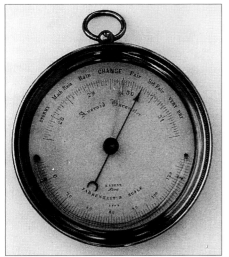
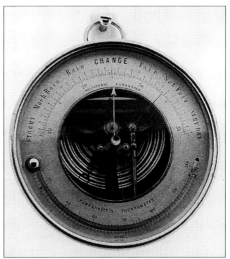

Above left, Fig. 4.1: *A 4.5 inch brass-cased aneroid by E. J. Dent, late 1840s.*
Above right, Fig. 4.2: *A 6 inch dial brass-cased aneroid, c.1860.*

Below left, Fig. 4.3: *An 8 inch brass-cased barometer, c. 1870.*
Below right, Fig. 4.4: *A 5 inch oak-cased ship's aneroid by Dollond, c. 1880.*

Above left, Fig. 4.5: *A Universal Barometer, c. 1880.*
Above right, Fig. 4.6: *Negretti & Zambra fisherman's aneroid, c. 1890.*

Below left, Fig. 4.7: *Dollond fisherman's aneroid, c. 1890.*
Below right, Fig. 4.8: *A 4.5 inch brass-cased card dial aneroid, c. 1869.*

on to the cardboard dial, interestingly now faded to a brown colour, whereas the remainder of the dial has remainded black. This example is a nice straightforward, honest, simple barometer of its period, around 1885.

Another type of dial used was clear glass. Fig. 4.10 is an example of an 8 inch dial aneroid barometer with completely open movement, the dial lettered in reverse on the back of the glass, circa 1870s. However, the very best-quality barometers were made with engraved brass and silvered dials. Fig. 4.11 illustrates a 4.5 inch dial precision compensated barometer by J. Hicks of London, dating from the late 1870s to 1880s, in a brass case, with finely engraved dial, very thin indicating hand and set hand, used for precision measurements. The mechanism of this barometer is of an exceptionally high degree of quality engineering as befits the maker, J. Hicks.

Aneroids were often sold in hinged boxes or with metal or wooden stands. Fig. 4.12 is a leather-cased 4.5 inch open dial barometer with curved mercury-filled thermometer, dated 1898, and inscribed with the retailer's name ' J. C. Vickery'. The leather carrying handle is missing, and the brass barometer is crudely mounted inside a wooden box which has been leather covered. Barometers usually have hand or hand and machine engraved dials until about 1920, as can be seen in Fig. 4.13. This 4.5 inch diameter brass aneroid barometer by C. W. Dixey of 3 New Bond Street, London, no. 1065, is a very late barometer, with the dial possibly chemically etched. Fig. 4.14 illustrates an early 1900 plain oak barometer with open card dial, 3 inch diameter, with two fixing plates, possibly for use on board a small boat. For larger boats or ships, a barometer like the one shown in Fig. 4.15 would have been bought: an 8 inch white glass dial ship's barometer by Kelvin & James White Ltd of Glasgow, circa 1913. The front bezel is hinged to allow access to the barometer dial and movement; and the large spun brass housing has four holes to fix to a mounting board or the side of the ship. The name is again lettered separately on the dial, indicating that this was made by another manufacturer and batched with the name of Kelvin & James White Ltd. Many similar models were made and sold for ships as well as land use, often without the hinged door and mounted on a piece of turned oak.

Meteorological Office barometers have been used for many years, their style not changing much over the decades and used for all types

Above left, Fig. 4.9: *A 4.5 inch brass-cased aneroid with retailer's name added in by hand, c. 1885.*

Above right, Fig. 4.10: *Glass dial brass-cased aneroid, c. 1875.*

Below left, Fig. 4.11: *A 4.5 inch dial precision aneroid by J. Hicks, c. 1875.*

Below right, Fig. 4.12: *Leather-cased desk barometer, dated 1898.*

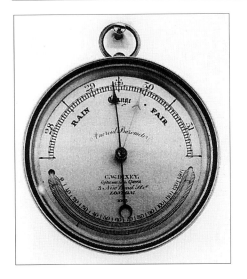

Above left, Fig. 4.13: *Etched dial brass-cased aneroid, c. 1920.*

Above right, Fig. 4.14: *A 3 inch card dial oak-cased barometer for small boat, c. 1910.*

Below left, Fig. 4.15: *An 8 inch white glass dial brass-cased ship's barometer, c. 1913.*

Below right, Fig. 4.16: *Mark II Met. Office pattern barometer, dated 1942.*

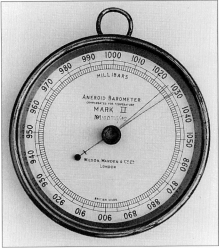

Above left, Fig. 4.17: *Mark II Met. Office pattern barometer, dated 1945.*

Above right, Fig. 4.18: *Mark II Met. Office pattern barometer, dated 1966.*

Below left, Fig. 4.19: *Mark II Met. Office pattern barometer, c. 1970.*

Below right, Fig. 4.20: *An 8 inch silvered engraved dial ship's barometer by Negretti & Zambra, c. 1950.*

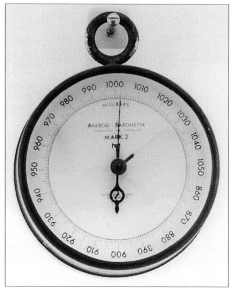 

Fig. 4.21:
An 8 inch printed dial ship's barometer by Lufft, c. 1970.

of marine and land use: some would have been used by harbour masters and the like. Most certainly not a domestic barometer, Fig. 4.16 is a 4.5 inch Mark II Met. Office barometer with printed aluminium dial, dated 1942, retailed by Wilson, Warden & Co. Ltd, London. A good-quality almost identical aneroid barometer is Fig. 4.17, a Met. Office 4.5 inch barometer with inches and millibar scale, in a brass case, with etched silvered brass dial, by Short & Mason, London, dated 1945. These two companies both manufactured in their own right, but whether they bought movements from each other will be difficult to ascertain without copies of purchase order books and so on. My own inclination is that Short & Mason made the movements and Wilson, Warden & Co. Ltd marketed this particular model, while making other instruments themselves. The Short & Mason barometer still hangs on to inches of mercury as well as the necessary millibars. The same pattern is illustrated in Fig. 4.18, a Met. Office 4.5 inch barometer Mark II, with millibar scale, in brass case, by Short & Mason, London, dated 1966, with painted metal face.

Fig. 4.19 shows a much later Met. Office 4.5 inch barometer Mark II, with millibar scale, printed on painted metal dial, by Shortland Bowen Instruments, circa 1970, with large fixed hanging ring. Nearly all these types of government standard barometer had individual instrument numbers marked on them, usually on the dial. The last two numbers denote the date; if two more are added this denotes a date when the barometer was recalibrated or tested. Barometers like the one shown in Fig. 4.20 were possibly bought for commercial shipping. It has an 8 inch diameter silvered dial with millibars and inches, and was made by Negretti & Zambra of London, compensated, possibly in the 1950s. It has a high-quality aneroid mechanism for a utility purpose. More recently, according to the owner, the barometer shown in Fig. 4.21 came from an oil tanker. Installed in about 1970, it is an 8 inch dial ship's barometer, made by Lufft of Germany. Interestingly, the glass on this barometer is crudely inscribed with the number of the barometer, although it is not visible in this photograph. The mechanism is of traditional, German high quality, and the bezel is chrome plated, as is the case, with three fixing holes, the divisions being Hectar-Pascalls (millibars) on the inside and millimetres of mercury on the outside.

Left: White glass 7 inch barometer in pierced and carved oak case, c. 1900.

Right: Enamelled 4.25 inch dial barometer with carved and turned decoration to the case of German origin, c. 1910.

Left: Clock, thermometer and barometer with 5 inch dial in an ornately carved oak case by Stanley of London, c. 1880.

Right: Ceramic 6 inch dial barometer in a carved oak case, c. 1895.

5 Pocket Barometers

It was not until the early 1860s that pocket barometers were made. Vidi's patent having expired, Negretti & Zambra worked to design a more portable barometer, and in 1864 they were advertising aneroid barometers from 1.25 inch to 6 inch diameter. The first of the smaller than 'Dent' barometers were probably as illustrated in Fig. 5.1, an early mountain pocket-sized barometer, with card dial. It measures 2.5 inches in diameter and is 1.125 inches thick, with a personalised inscription of 1863. I have not come across any earlier small barometers. It was probably this type that was advertised as the newest in small portable aneroid barometers by Negretti & Zambra, but it was soon produced even smaller. By the late 1860s, there was a profusion of pocket aneroids available. In *How to Use the Barometer* by Rev. R. Tyas, dated 1866, the mountain barometer is illustrated, similar to Fig. 5.1 and described in brief. Since in 1864 Negretti & Zambra were advertising pocket barometers from 1.25 inches diameter, I think it is reasonable to assume that Tyas's annual publication of 1866 would be using illustrations of a few years earlier. This type of mountain barometer does not always have any altitude scale marked on it; instead, one has to calculate from the barometric pressure (as one would have done with a mercurial barometer) the altitude to which you have ascended or descended. The inscription on the barometer in Fig. 5.1 shows that this type of mountain barometer actually dates from 23rd November 1863 when it was presented. The registered design lozenge is dated 11th January 1862, being the design date and not the manufacturing date.

The next size of pocket barometer to be made is likely to be as illustrated in Fig. 5.2, which shows a fine pocket barometer with a delicate curved mercury-filled thermometer by Carpenter & Westley, compensated, without altitude scale, dated on the reverse 1869. It measures 2 inches in diameter and is seven-eighths of an inch thick; the sides are straight and the case was made for it, not as some later

Above left, Fig. 5.1: *Early brass-cased mountain barometer 2.5 inch diameter, inscribed 1863.*
Above right, Fig. 5.2: *Square-sided brass-cased barometer 2 inch diameter by Carpenter & Westley, inscribed 1869.*
Below left, Fig. 5.3: *Enamel dial pocket watch-style case with 1.75 inch diameter dial, c. 1880.*
Below right, Fig. 5.4: *Brass-cased barometer 1.75 inch diameter with compass on dial, dated 1866.*

ones, which were made from pocket watch cases. Fig. 5.3 illustrates a case that could equally be made for a pocket watch: it has a 1.75 inch enamel dial in a gilded brass case. In fact, about 95 per cent of pocket barometers have gilded brass cases; some are silver cased, a very few are gold cased and some industrial ones have blued brass cases. Much later ones have polished brass cases – usually twentieth-century barometers – and occasionally one finds nickel and silver-plated items. This particular barometer dates from around 1880, with no altitude scale, and weather indications and barometric measurements from 25 to 31 inches; the revolving index pointer is on the bezel. The majority of pocket barometers have engraved silvered dials which makes this barometer slightly rare. As already mentioned, by the late 1860s there was a profusion of small pocket barometers in all types of cases, sizes and for different uses. Fig. 5.4 shows an interesting barometer with a 1.75 inch silvered brass dial in a gilded brass case, mounted with a very small compass on the dial and, on the reverse, 'For progress in navigation, HMS Britannia, 1866'; the hand is not the original.

The cased pocket barometer shown in Fig. 5.5 is by Negretti & Zambra, no. 5072, with altitude scale from zero to 10,000 feet. The case can be seen with trade label and coat of arms, and, although worn, is in generally good condition. This example possibly dates from the first half of the 1860s, the dial is nicely engraved by hand and the barometer apparently not compensated for temperature change. Shown in Fig. 5.6 is another Negretti & Zambra of London pocket barometer, no. 20512, with trade mark underneath, this time compensated, with an altitude scale from 0 to 3,000 feet. In a 2.625 inch diameter case, 1.125 inches thick, it possibly dates from the first half of the 1870s.

The unsigned barometer shown in Fig. 5.7 is made with a revolving altitude scale from 0 to 8,000 feet, with curved mercury-filled thermometer in its original case, circa early 1870s. Notice the different design of case where it has a lug to conceal the carrying ring, whereas previous illustrations have shown simple round cases with the ring projecting through the case. I have not been able to determine which style was earlier, and I have come to the conclusion that they were probably both offered as cases, the simple round case enabling the barometer to be carried on a chain and affording protection of the barometer. Considering the poor condition of some of these cases, this

Above, Fig. 5.5: *Cased Negretti & Zambra barometer, c. 1865.*

Below, Fig. 5.6: *A 2.625 inch diameter barometer by Negretti & Zambra, c. 1870.*

was certainly one of their uses. It is also interesting to note that on many of these cases there is a small brass button which was originally covered over during the manufacture of the case. Pressing this button underneath the leather would open the case. The majority of cases have suffered the loss of this button due to wearing of the leather through use and the button falling out. It is therefore nice, on those rare occasions, to find a case in good condition, with the button still covered over as originally made. This only goes to show, however, that the owner did not use it much – perhaps it was a gift to an unappreciative recipient. Note the shape of the hand: the majority of hands are round or crescent, but this is spear shaped.

Among the rarer pocket barometers are the very small ones. Although they were advertised for sale, the small number that survive perhaps indicates that fewer were bought. By far the majority are 1.75 inches to 2 inches in diameter, with many larger odd sizes, probably because the smaller ones were thought not to be so good and were perhaps regarded as more of an ornament. The 1.25 inch silvered dial pocket barometer in silver case, by J.H. Steward, 456 West Strand, London, circa 1880, shown in Fig. 5.8, is a fine example except that it is missing the suspension ring. The smallest barometer I have come across is operational but is far more a decorative toy than a serious instrument. It is illustrated in Fig. 5.9, an 18ct gold ladies' barometer with a 0.875 inch gilded engraved dial, circa 1920s. I have heard that even smaller barometers were made but have not, as yet, seen one.

Many pocket barometers were fitted with thermometers originally to compensate for temperature changes. The only one I have seen to be fitted with a dial thermometer is illustrated in Fig. 5.10, a 1.75 inch silvered brass dial barometer in gilded brass case with dial thermometer mounted within the barometer dial, by Watson Brothers, 31 Cockspur Street, London, circa 1894. The dial tells us that this is patent 7318, which almost certainly refers to the thermometer, but I have not yet found the relevant patent details without the exact year that the patent was filed. The maker's or retailer's name adds interest and value to most barometers as does an original case with names and labels. Figs 5.11 and 5.12 show, first, a pocket aneroid by Dollond & Co., 62 Old Broad Street, with the original trade label stuck into the hinged lid, compensated, with no. 12293 stamped on the dial, the altitude range from 0 to 12,000 feet, dating from around 1890; the

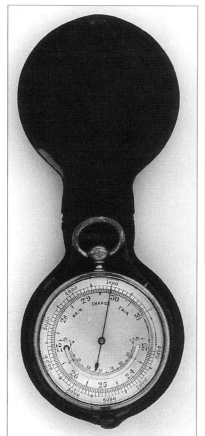

Opposite above left, Fig. 5.7: *Fully cased barometer 1.75 inch diameter with thermometer, c. 1875.*
Opposite above right, Fig. 5.8: *A 1.25 inch dial silver barometer by J.H. Steward, c. 1880.*
Opposite below left, Fig. 5.9: *A 0.875 inch diameter dial ladies' 18ct gold-cased barometer, c. 1920.*
Opposite below right, Fig. 5.10: *Barometer with dial thermometer mounted on dial, c. 1894.*

Below left, Fig. 5.11: *Cased Dollond barometer, c. 1890.*
Below right, Fig. 5.12: *Cased Aitchison & Co. barometer, c. 1900.*

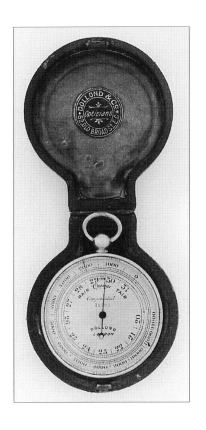

second is a pocket barometer by Aitchison & Co., probably dating from the early twentieth century. This model is mounted with a mercury-filled curved thermometer, an altitude scale from 0 to 8,000 feet, with embossed trade mark and name on the silk-lined case. It is interesting to note that the firm of Dollond & Co. and Aitchison & Co. later became known as Dollond & Aitchison, the high street opticians in business today.

Perhaps a slightly more unusual barometer is illustrated in Fig. 5.13, being a Hicks' Patent altitude meter with 2.75 inch dial, a typical pocket barometer but this time with no weather indications, the dial being divided from 0 to 2,500 feet, half for ascent and half for descent. It is difficult to imagine much use other than in mines for the descent scale unless for some simple surveying or engineering work. It probably dates from around 1890. The barometer shown in Fig. 5.14 is possibly from 1895, a late Victorian open dial pocket barometer of 1.75 inch diameter with semi-circular curved thermometer. (The thermometer does not quite fit: the end of the tube does not sit into the locating hole near 140°F – a sign of poor workmanship or a later replacement?) The dial does not have altitude markings, but the open dial makes it a very attractive item.

Fig. 5.15 illustrates an interesting silver-cased pocket barometer with altitude scale from 0 to 8,000 feet and adjustable by means of the knurled winding mechanism. The 'winder' and ring on this model are in a plated steel, the rest of the barometer case being in silver, possibly dating from 1895. The altitude ring on this type of barometer was usually made into an L-shaped cross-section and cut into a rack (teethed) to fit into a pinion on the end of the winding stem. Thus, turning the stem left or right turns the altitude scale. Many of these silver cases were adapted from normal pocket watch cases of the day. This can also be seen in Fig. 5.16 which shows the reverse of a silver pocket barometer by Hicks of London, with nicely engraved personal initials and clearly showing the hallmark of London, dated 1891. Fig. 5.17 shows the dial of the Hicks silver pocket barometer with the Watkin patent originating from 1886 (see Appendix). Hicks, being an exemplary maker, shows his skills in this particular case, dial and mechanism. The movement of this barometer, as previously described on larger models, is designed to allow the needle to move twice around the dial. It is hard for us to appreciate the market in Victorian days,

Fig. 5.13: *Hicks' Patent altitude meter, c. 1890.*

Fig. 5.14: *Open dial barometer, c. 1890.*

Above, Fig. 5.15: *Cased barometer with winder to turn altitude scale, c. 1895.*

Below left, Fig. 5.16: *Rear view of Hicks barometer case, dated 1891.*

Below right, Fig. 5.17: *Front view of dial of Hicks barometer, dated 1891.*

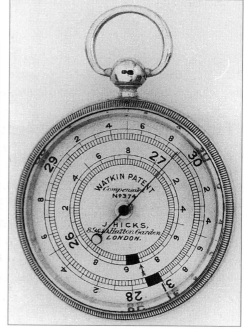

but we can perhaps imagine the competing manufacturers of these items constantly bringing out new models to try to capture a larger market. The amount of work involved to produce some of these items – many of which we will probably never find or only see once or twice – makes it difficult for us to understand how they could have made much money. But, presumably, with labour costs low and an affluent London society, there was profit at the end of the day.

A fairly rare and highly collectable piece is the small, egg-shaped pocket barometer compendium set illustrated in Fig. 5.18. With mother-of-pearl compass and ivory scale thermometer, it is by Chadburn's Ltd, 47 Castle Street, Liverpool, circa 1880s. This is a fine example from Chadburn's, who are among my favourite manufacturers. An even rarer version is the three-piece compendium set shown in Fig. 5.19, the three instruments being the thermometer, barometer and compass, each in a separate silver case 1 inch in diameter. Single-piece compendiums are also well sought after, making a good addition to any small collection of pocket barometers. Fig. 5.20 is a pocket barometer by Ross with altitude scale from 0 to 10,000 feet, compensated, circa 1880, while Fig. 5.21 shows the reverse, with mother-of-pearl compass in the centre and almost circular mercury-filled thermometer on silvered scale. This would originally have been supplied in a leather carrying case with two hinged lids, similar to the one illustrated in Fig. 5.22, which gives the reverse of the barometer shown in Fig. 5.11, with a compass and thermometer, dated 1890s. This time, instead of a round ball thermometer, it has a cylindrical reservoir to the thermometer, itself curved, which is more unusual. Another variation of the compendium barometer is the one shown in Fig. 5.23, a rear view of a pocket barometer by Negretti & Zambra. The compass is visible through a hole in the back of the carrying case.

When the carrying cases of these barometers survive, not only does it improve the value of the item but, in most instances, it means that the actual barometer has been kept well and is less oxidised than one that has been kept in a drawer or in a pocket. The condition of these are sometimes almost mint, having been bought and perhaps never used, tucked away in a cabinet or drawer. This, of course, should also be a warning: if you find a pocket barometer on sale with a case and the case is in good order but the pocket barometer is badly worn, it

Above, Fig. 5.18: *Oval compendium set barometer, thermometer and compass by Chadburn's Ltd, c. 1880.*

Below, Fig. 5.19: *Oval compendium set barometer, thermometer and compass in separate silver cases, c. 1900.*

Above left, Fig. 5.20: *Front view of compendium barometer by Ross, c. 1880.*

Above right, Fig. 5.21: *Rear view of compendium barometer by Ross, c. 1880.*

Below right, Fig. 5.22: *Rear view of a compendium by Dollond in case (as Fig. 5.11), c. 1890.*

Below left, Fig. 5.23: *Rear view of Negretti & Zambra barometer showing the compass, c. 1897.*

may well be that the case is not original. If the barometer is worn then it is normal to find the case quite worn as well. When they have been left open for some time, perhaps on a shelf, then ultraviolet rays have usually discoloured the lining, which in its original state would have been very plush and richly coloured. The linings are normally green, red or blue, and the leather case is usually of dark red morocco leather, although sometimes black or brown.

Most pocket barometers have altitude scales and these revolve for setting. Fig. 5.24 shows a 1.75 inch silvered brass dial pocket barometer with altitude scale up to 8,000 feet and down to 1,000 feet below sea level, by J.H. Steward Ltd of London, circa 1915. The dial is of one piece without any revolving altitude scale, which must have made it a cheaper item, and the case is considerably worn. The barometer in Fig. 5.25 is a later, and perhaps cheaper, barometer. It has a 1.75 inch diameter acid-etched (processed) silvered brass dial with revolving altitude scale from 0 to 8,000 feet by Short & Mason, sold by A. & N.C.S. Ltd at Westminster, circa 1930s, in original morocco-covered case.

Many manufacturers, having survived the revolution from mercury to aneroid, seem to have carried on well into the twentieth century. The barometers we are discussing in this book were, in their day, a very important item and, from the range of surviving examples, one can begin to see what a large array was on offer to the prospective purchaser. I have been fortunate to collect over the years several trade catalogues; one of the most interesting is by F. Darton & Co. of about 1910, when they were in the Clerkenwell area of London, which illustrates many varied barometers and instruments. F. Darton & Co. were perhaps one of the leading manufacturers between 1880 and 1920 who would have sold to Negretti & Zambra and many other producers. I have it on good authority that Darton rarely put their name on items until the twentieth century and then only by means of their trademark, being a picture of a dart with the letters 'O N' at the bottom, most commonly seen on their scientific Fortin and Kew barometers. It is particularly interesting to note in the Darton catalogue that even into the 1970s they were advertising pocket barometers, although I do not believe that these were actually available to buy for all that long after the catalogue was issued and probably consisted of a certain amount of old stock. Darton, being a

Above, Fig. 5.24: *Simple barometer with one piece dial by J. H. Steward, c. 1915.*

Below, Fig. 5.25: *Etched dial barometer with revolving altitude scale by Short & Mason, c. 1930.*

very old established firm, had masses of equipment and bits and pieces which, during the past decade, were largely disposed of. It is purely through good fortune that I have been able to gain some insight into the Darton firm through one of its shareholders who has been connected with the firm for most of this century. From the description of the variety of instruments made by them around the turn of the century, many of which can be recognised in this book as well as in markets and auction rooms, they appear to be a much underestimated company.

Glancing through the preceding illustrations, it will become apparent that there is little standard in altitude scales. This is probably due to the fact that one could buy a variety of designs in a variety of altitude scales perhaps for the ordinary walker or for the person going on an expedition or high-altitude walking. The advantages of having a lower altitude reading is that you can see more movement in the needle, but, if one wants to go to higher altitudes, then the normal variations of pressure at any set altitude will be a lot closer together and the normal movements of the barometer will be harder to see on a more expanded scale than those with a lower altitude reading.

6 Banjo-shaped Aneroid Barometers

Most aneroid barometers in wooden cases tend to be of the banjo style. This is understandable due to the development of the mercury wheel barometer into the banjo shape, which became the classic style of barometer. Although early aneroids were made in brass cases, such as the Dent barometers and pocket barometers, and there were, indeed, table and shelf barometers of numerous shapes and sizes, the big advantage of the aneroid – that it is portable, as opposed to the mercury barometer – lent itself to the aneroid mechanism being inserted underneath the dial to simulate mercury barometers of the period. So, it is not uncommon to find the early styles of banjo aneroid barometers being similar in design to their mercury counterparts.

Fig. 6.1, for example, shows a card dial banjo-shaped aneroid barometer in mahogany, carved to a very traditional design which could easily be found on a mercury barometer, although this one is only about 22 inches long. It probably dates from around 1860. Fig. 6.2 shows a heavily carved oak aneroid barometer, with a ceramic open 8 inch dial, and spiral thermometer, of a typical Victorian Gothic style, available from around 1865. The majority of these open dial barometers had exceptionally good-quality movements, usually with the springs plated and all brass pieces polished and lacquered to a high degree, sometimes even gold plated, the steel, where necessary, being glued and lacquered. The largest mahogany barometer I have handled is the splendid Victorian deeply carved mahogany barometer shown in Fig. 6.3, with ceramic curved open dial and ceramic thermometer scale. The case measures approximately 13 inches by 44 inches and is 3 inches thick, weighing in at 19lb (8.5 kilos).This barometer has all the hallmarks of grandiose Victorian items, including the vase of flowers carved in the case beneath the dial!

A type of barometer I have only seen once is illustrated in Fig. 6.4,

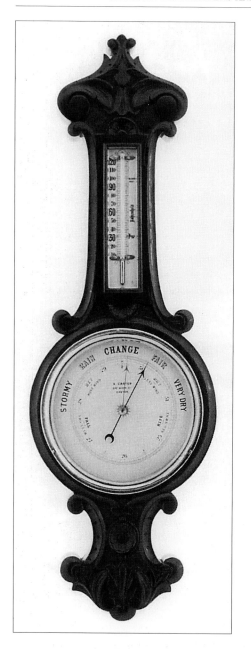

Left, Fig. 6.1: *Mahogany carved barometer, 22 inches long, c. 1860.*

Right, Fig. 6.2: *Heavily carved oak barometer with open dial, c. 1865.*

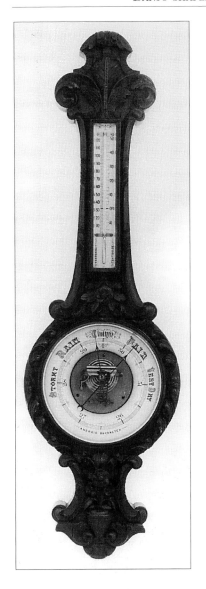 

Left, Fig. 6.3: *A large carved mahogany barometer with 10 inch dial, c. 1868.*

Right, Fig. 6.4: *An 8 inch composite glass dial ebonised barometer, c. 1860.*

an 8 inch dial, ebonised carved case banjo barometer by Chadburn Brothers, Liverpool. This is a very unusual barometer in terms of its dial and thermometer scale, being clear glass with a blue paper background, making it appear to be blue glass but with white glass flashed on to the front of the scales, with the numbers, divisions and letters hand-lettered and fired into the glass. It is perhaps typical of 1860 designs of cases. Another similar case, though much larger, is shown in Fig. 6.5, a 10 inch dial aneroid barometer in carved oak case, dating from about 1875, with ceramic dials. Very few 10 inch aneroid barometers appear to have been made, judging by the surviving numbers seen. This one is again a classic style based on the mercury banjo of the early to mid-Victorian period. The simple style of the indicating hand leads me to think that this is later than the barometer illustrated in Fig. 6.4.

Fig. 6.6 shows a good example of a solid oak aneroid barometer with printed card dial and silvered brass thermometer scale, applied C-scroll mouldings and visible movement. At a distance, across a saleroom, one could be forgiven for thinking this is a mercury barometer. It is only some 2 inches shorter than the usual full-size mercury barometer and dates from around 1875. A barometer in a highly ornate carved oak case is illustrated in Fig. 6.7. This aneroid barometer dates from about 1875–85, with 8 inch ceramic dial, and it is obvious from the style that, although probably English made, it was heavily influenced by continental designs. It is, I think, the only illustration of a barometer in this style of banjo case that is non-symmetrical. Certainly continental in design is Fig. 6.8, a 6 inch dial cast bronze and brass barometer of probably French origin, c. 1870, the case depicting tassels, ribbons and foliage. The barometer has an open card dial and utilises a high-quality movement. Returning to a more British style, we see, in Fig. 6.9, a 5 inch card dial ornately carved oak combination barometer, with 4 inch enamel clock face and ivory thermometer scale with decorative brass cover to the mercury bulb. The case has well-executed carving of rope and anchor design by Stanley of London, c. 1880. Still on a nautical theme is Fig. 6.10, a 6 inch dial 'anchor' clock and barometer, the clock and the barometer having enamelled dials, by G. J. Tilling & Sons of Southampton, with pseudo coat-of-arms above the clock. This is a typical Victorian design barometer of around 1875–90. A good-quality early design banjo-

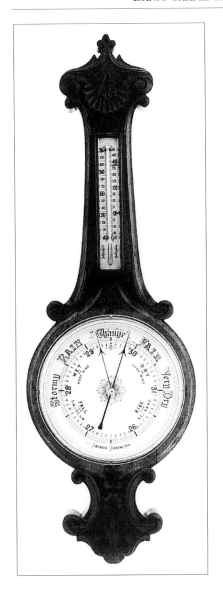 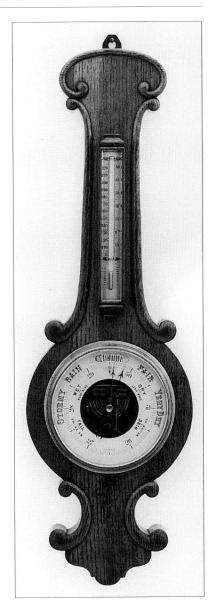

Left, Fig. 6.5: *A 10 inch ceramic dial oak carved barometer, c. 1875.*

Right, Fig. 6.6: *Mercury-style cased aneroid barometer with open dial, c. 1875.*

 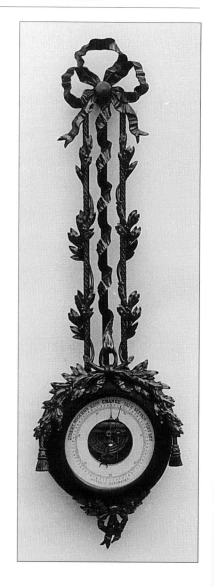

Left, Fig. 6.7: *Ornate carved 8 inch dial barometer, c. 1880.*

Right, Fig. 6.8: *Cast bronze and brass barometer with 6 inch card dial, c. 1870.*

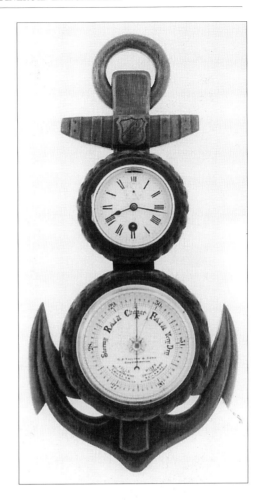

Left, Fig. 6.9: *A 5 inch card dial clock, thermometer and barometer by Stanley of London, c. 1880.*

Right, Fig. 6.10: *A 6 inch enamel dial clock barometer, c. 1885.*

shaped aneroid is illustrated in Fig. 6.11, probably from 1865, by Marratt & Ellis. The pine case is veneered in walnut with applied C-scroll mouldings, and it has an engraved silvered 8 inch dial and thermometer scale, the bezel bolted through the case. The whole is of very high quality and highly collectable.

Highly uncollectable in my eyes are the cast-iron barometers that occasionally turn up at auction. Fig. 6.12 is the most common design, a 4.5 inch dial cast-iron barometer and clock by J.J. Wainwright & Co., Birmingham, circa 1875. This one has been later painted gold. The aneroid mechanism is behind a printed card scale, the thermometer is silvered brass and the clock dial is enamel: it is quite unusual to have a mixture of three materials for different dials. This type of barometer is naturally susceptible to damage by cracking if dropped, but otherwise usually survive intact, being exceptionally heavy. Fig. 6.13 shows a similar 4.5 inch dial cast-iron barometer, possibly earlier (1870), in a different design of case, by J.J. Wainwright. The aneroid movement is again behind a printed card scale, the thermometer is missing on this one, which has a brass engraved scale, the clock of a painted and printed dial. The case in original condition was burnished and hand gilded in some areas only; it is now sadly in a poor state but far preferable to painting with gold paint! Fig 6.14 is quite an unusual style cast-iron clock, barometer and thermometer, in the form of the Royal Coat of Arms. The aneroid movement is French, as most of these types are; the clock without a strike has an enamel 4.75 inch dial, the 3.5 inch barometer dial is printed card and the thermometer was probably the usual silvered brass scale but has been replaced by a much later type. This example of 'Victoriana' is nearly 12 inches wide by 25 inches long and weighs 10 lb (4.5 kilos).

Fig. 6.15 is an 8 inch ceramic dial oak-cased barometer and thermometer of late Victorian style, circa 1880, with floral garlands extending from the thermometer box to pillars above the dial, with leaf and scroll carving profusely prominent. Fig. 6.16 illustrates an 8 inch ceramic dial barometer and thermometer, circa 1880, with ornately carved oak case and applied mouldings to the top and bottom of the barometer dial. The dial also has some wind indications for falling or rising barometer; these are attributed to Admiral Fitzroy and can often be found added to aneroid barometers. A very common dial design can be seen in Fig. 6.17, an 8 inch ceramic dial, with initial

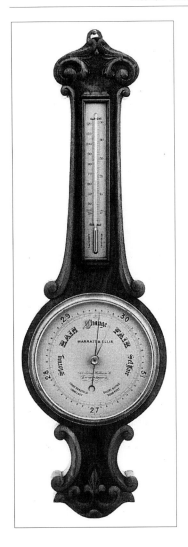 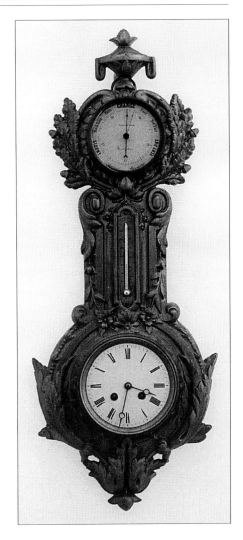

Left, Fig. 6.11: *A walnut veneered barometer with 8 inch engraved silvered dial by Marratt & Ellis, c. 1865.*

Right, Fig. 6.12: *A 4.5 inch dial cast-iron barometer, thermometer and clock by J. J. Wainwright, c. 1875.*

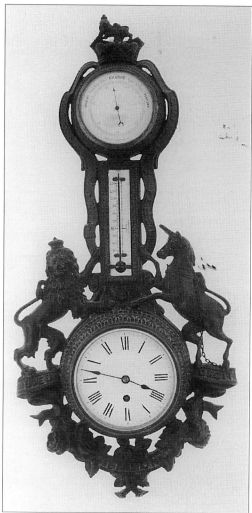

Left, Fig. 6.13: *Cast-iron 4.5 inch dial barometer, thermometer and clock by J. J. Wainwright, c. 1870.*

Right, Fig. 6.14: *A 4.5 inch dial cast-iron barometer, thermometer and clock, unnamed, c. 1880.*

 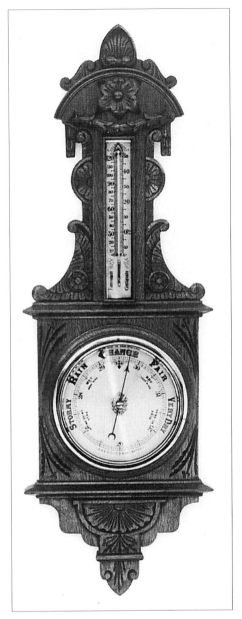

Left, Fig. 6.15: *Barometer with 8 inch ceramic dial in carved oak case, c. 1880.*

Right, Fig. 6.16: *An 8 inch ceramic dial barometer in carved oak case, with applied turned decoration, c. 1880.*

letters and numbers painted red by hand. This is an oak-cased barometer and thermometer with columns and finials of a late Victorian style, circa 1890. The dial is almost framed by the applied moulding and turned pillars. The next barometer iillustrated is an elaborate American walnut aneroid barometer (Fig. 6.18) with thermometer, with spiral tube, Corinthian column effect case, surmounted by pediment with carved urn finial, the dial and scale with silvered brass engraved. Sometimes these have red wax as well as black wax filled engraving. This one probably dates from around 1890.

The largest aneroid barometer I have handled is illustrated in Fig. 6.19, an enormous 12 inch dial Victorian Gothic oak barometer of the early 1890s by T. Armstrong & Brothers of Manchester, measuring 15 inches wide by 51 inches in height, constructed from pieces of solid oak, carved, turned and cut into a pattern typifying the style of the Late Victorian period, perhaps to excess. It weighs nearly 13 kilos (28.5lb)! The dial has extremely well-executed engraving both to the centre of the dial, which is not wax filled, and to the letters 'Rain', 'Fair' and 'Change'. It has an exceptionally large spiral thermometer and a pediment of castellated style. A particularly interesting detail is the indicating hand which is usually of blued steel. This one, being larger and therefore heavier than the normal shorter hands for 8 and 10 inch dials, has been made from aluminium, a metal that was probably quite expensive and rather new as it is seldom found on Victorian barometers. This is an important factor as far as the operation of the movement is concerned because only a normal size mechanism is used in this 'Goliath'. This example certainly dwarfs most aneroid barometers, although one comes across similar mercury edifices from time to time: they are seldom very saleable.

At the other extreme of size, Fig. 6.20 shows a miniature banjo design aneroid barometer by the same maker as Fig. 6.19, measuring 9 inches by 2.5 inches, possibly a little later in date at about 1900, one of those unusual Victorian small or miniature pieces that are very hard to find. The aneroid movement is an adapted pocket barometer with straight-sided case, and knurled revolving bezel with pointer to use for setting the barometer each day. It has an inner silvered ring that would normally be engraved with altitude markings but would not be needed for this item. It is made from boxwood and is

Left, Fig. 6.17: *An 8 inch ceramic dial barometer in carved oak case, with applied carved turned pillars, c. 1890.*

Right, Fig. 6.18: *American walnut barometer with 8 inch silvered engraved dial, c. 1890.*

very finely carved, being an extremely good example of what was available in larger sizes. I consider it likely that these may have been travellers' show pieces. The quality of this piece is so good, and the detail of the carving is just like its larger versions.

Returning to more regular-sized barometers, Fig. 6.21 is an example of a late Victorian and early Edwardian barometer in carved oak case with leaves and scrolls. Towards the base of the barometer can be seen a typical imitation scroll which is a characteristic feature of some barometers. Fig. 6.22 shows an 8 inch ceramic dial ash-cased barometer and thermometer of typical Art Nouveau design, circa 1890. The pierced carved scrolls and decoration of Fig. 6.23 make a slightly different design for an oak aneroid barometer and thermometer, this one with porcelain scales, circa 1890. Yet another design with scrolls and leaf decoration can be seen in Fig. 6.24, an 8 inch ceramic dial oak-cased barometer and thermometer of late Victorian style, circa 1895, the carving blending into the shaped case with incised decoration. Although I think that aneroid barometers with engraved silvered dials are generally earlier than the ceramic type, it must have been possible for many years to purchase either style perhaps to order with any dial of your choice, especially if you were buying direct from a maker. Fig. 6.25 is an 8 inch silvered brass dial oak-cased barometer and thermometer of late Victorian style, circa 1885; the carved case has applied fluted decorations and mouldings. It could perhaps be slightly earlier, but I would imagine that you could find examples of the same case with a ceramic dial. The style of Fig. 6.26 shows a distinct change in case-making. If you compare this barometer with previous illustrations, this 8 inch dial barometer of around 1900 not only has a cheaper cardboard dial and thermometer scale but the carving is applied to the oak case in quite an obvious manner. One cannot be certain about dating as so many designs continued to be used for decades, but the dials continually changed and cardboard was reintroduced at different periods, probably due to cost. The barometer illustrated is a classic example of trying to reduce the cost as opposed to using ceramic or other materials, although the maker has gone to the trouble of using red and black coloured ink for printing. Fig. 6.27 also shows this later design of applied carving but mixes a little by carving the top of the crests and is generally a good 8 inch silvered brass dial American walnut-cased barometer and

 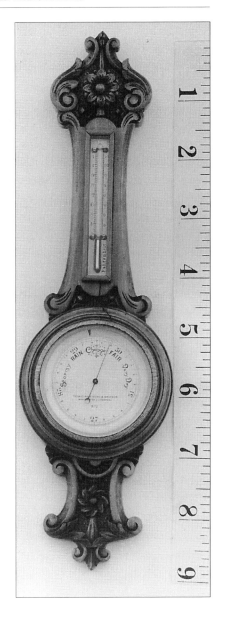

Left, Fig. 6.19: *Gothic-style 12 inch dial barometer in oak case, c. 1890.*

Right, Fig. 6.20: *Miniature barometer in boxwood case by T. Armstrong and Brothers, Manchester, c. 1900.*

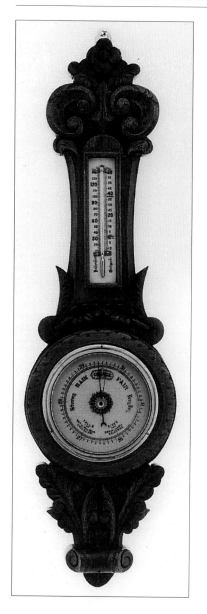 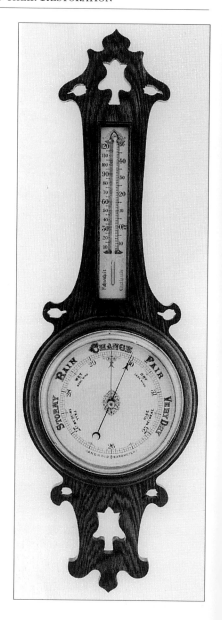

Left, Fig. 6.21: *A 6 inch white glass dial barometer in carved oak case, c. 1900.*

Right, Fig. 6.22: *Carved ash 8 inch dial barometer with thermometer and carved swags, c. 1890.*

Above: Silvered and engraved 6 inch open dial barometer with expanded scale in a brass case of French origin, c. 1880.

Below: A nautically inspired brass-cased barometer depicting cannons, ship's wheel and anchor with 3.25 inch enamelled dial, c. 1890.

Above: Brass-cased 4.75 inch dial barometer retailed by Husbands of Bristol, c. 1895.

Below: An early Dent-style barometer with unusual 4 inch card dial in a square carrying case numbered 1815, unsigned, c. 1846.

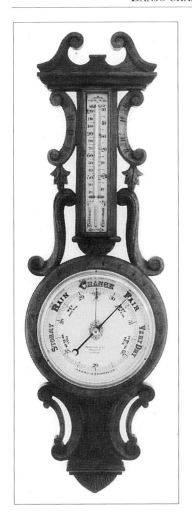

Left, Fig. 6.23: *An 8 inch ceramic dial oak-carved barometer with pierced carving and swan neck pediment, c. 1890.*

Right, Fig. 6.24: *Carved oak 8 inch ceramic dial barometer, c. 1895.*

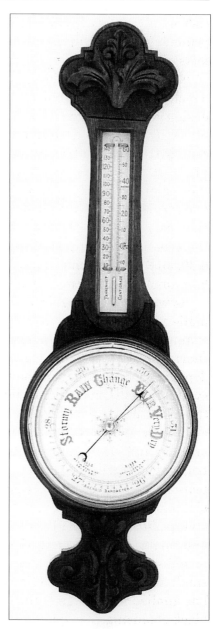

Left, Fig. 6.25: *Oak-cased 8 inch engraved silvered dial barometer, c. 1885.*

Right, Fig. 6.26: *An 8 inch cardboard dial oak-cased barometer with applied carvings, c. 1900.*

thermometer of early twentieth-century style, circa 1910, with pseudo pediment, missing finial, and a thermometer of spiral design presently missing its box.

A very traditional design of case is illustrated in Fig. 6.28, an 8 inch ceramic dial barometer and thermometer of traditional lozenge design pediment, circa 1900. The dials of these types are usually only black printing and they commonly use white glass or even a combination as the transition from ceramic to white glass occurred. Fig. 6.29 is another 8 inch ceramic dial oak-cased barometer and thermometer of early twentieth-century style, circa 1900, with pierced and carved case with applied triangular carved moulding. The rather obviously added, although original, incised carved pediment spoils the good line of the rest of the case. The more classic design of Fig. 6.30, an 8 inch ceramic dial oak-cased barometer and thermometer of late nineteenth-century style, is similar but better executed.

As was popular in Edwardian furniture, the barometer was often made with the use of inlay for decoration: Fig. 6.31 is an extant example of this craft. It has a 6 inch engraved silvered dial and thermometer scale with coloured wood and engraved ivory inlay depicting good weather and bad weather scenes along with other items: even the scrolls on the pediment are veneered in satinwood – probably the nicest example of an aneroid barometer that I have found. They also occasionally appear in 8 inch ceramic dials but, like many pieces, antique and clock dealers often take them home for themselves, a true sign of quality. Even very good inlaid barometers seem a little plain in comparison with the one shown in Fig. 6.32, an 8 inch ceramic dial inlaid Edwardian barometer, with thermometer scale and pagoda-style pediment, circa 1910, made from mahogany with rosewood veneer and coloured wood inlays. Usually boxwood and coloured woods are mixed with some ebony, and occasionally this style is found with a small amount of mother-of-pearl or ivory on. This particular design has applied mouldings at the top, usually crudely painted or stained black ebonizing. The quality of inlays varies. They are also available with 5 inch and 6 inch dials, sometimes brass and white glass. Fig. 6.33 is an 8 inch silvered brass (etched) dial in rosewood veneered mahogany case with soft metal inlays and mother-of-pearl. The case with architectural pediment simulating mercury barometers, circa 1920s, is by Dollond of London; the bezel is unusually of chromium

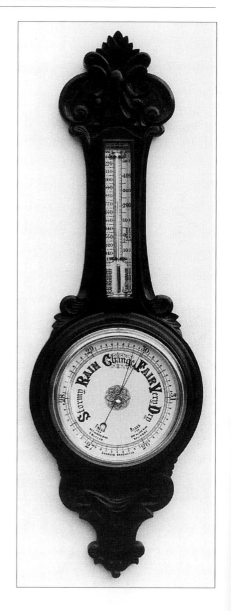

Left, Fig. 6.27: *American walnut barometer with 8 inch silvered brass dial, c. 1910.*

Right, Fig. 6.28: *An 8 inch ceramic dial in a very traditional lozenge and swags design case, c. 1900.*

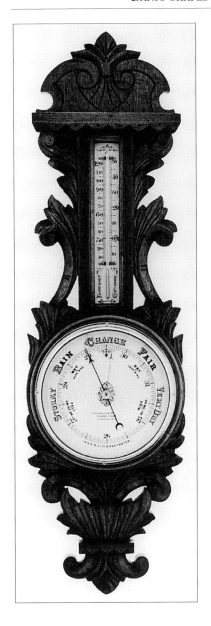 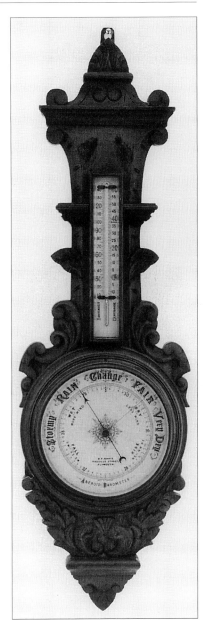

Left, Fig. 6.29: *An 8 inch ceramic dial carved oak-cased barometer with incised pediment, c. 1900.*

Right, Fig. 6.30: *Carved oak 8 inch ceramic dial barometer, c. 1898.*

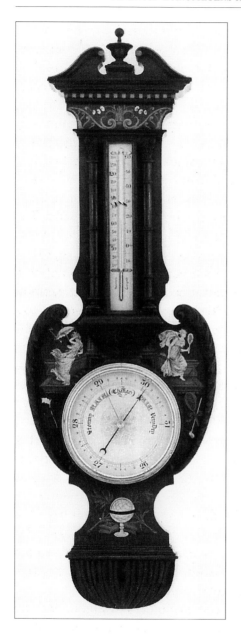
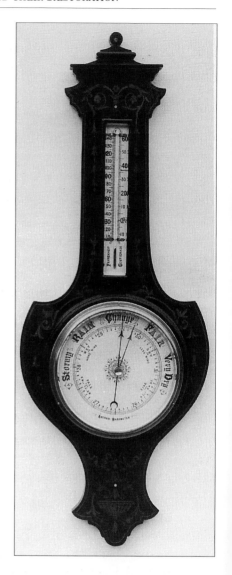

Left, Fig. 6.31: *Inlaid rosewood barometer with 6 inch engraved dial, c. 1910.*

Right, Fig. 6.32: *Ceramic 8 inch dial rosewood inlaid barometer, c. 1910.*

plate. Fig. 6.34 illustrates a quite typical Edwardian banjo barometer and thermometer with, unusually, an 8 inch printed silver dial, oak-cased, of circa 1920s. The case is of 1 inch thick oak with applied floral carving just above the thermometer, the remainder of the carving cut into the case.

Some styles of barometer were made for many years varying only slightly during particular periods such as the Edwardian Age and the Second World War. Many barometer styles remained in fashion, despite the influence of Art Deco and other movements. Barometer designs are for a reasonably traditional market so it is difficult to be exact when dating them, particularly in the 1920s and 1930s. The following barometers I have dated to the 1920s, but they could equally be found in the 1930s. There was also a variety of sizes in this period, as Fig. 6.35 illustrates, being a 4.5 inch ceramic dial barometer in simple carved oak case; the thermometer scale is of white glass now usual at this time. The dial of Fig. 6.36 shows a change in design to a simpler less fussy dial: only three weather words and notice how the divisions are spaced further around the dial more like a mercury barometer. This 1920s 8 inch white glass dial barometer is finished in a dark oak colour and has simple applied carvings. Fig. 6.37 varies in the use of printed dials on white painted metal. It is still fitted with an 8 inch dial but this particular design of dial appears any number of times in the 1930s and early 1950s, usually with Short & Mason printed on it, whom I believe produced some or all of this barometer. Comparing the dial of Fig. 6.38 with most other dials so far illustrated, you should be able to see the unusual position of the 30 inch mark, being at the top of the dial, and the variation from the normal weather words mixed with some of Admiral Fitzroy's remarks: 'Dull, Wet or More Wind' around 29 inches, 'Fair Generally' around 30 inches and 'Fine, Dry or Less Wind' around 31 inches. This variation makes a rather plain barometer slightly more interesting.

Slightly misleading at first sight, the barometer in Fig. 6.39 is an 8 inch etched brass dial barometer in heavily carved oak case, with a replacement thermometer and scale. Although the carved case is similar to Victorian items, this is indeed a good-quality late 1920s case barometer, the dial almost certainly by Short & Mason although inscribed with the retailer's name in this instance. It is probably an effort to reproduce an earlier style or what is sometimes called

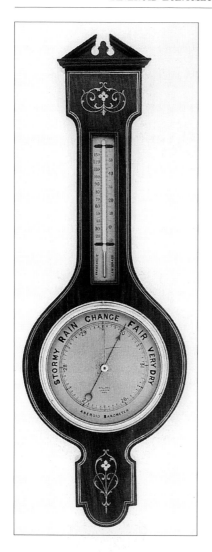

Left, Fig. 6.33: *Etched silvered 8 inch dial barometer with soft metal inlay (pewter), c. 1920.*

Right, Fig. 6.34: *Printed silvered 8 inch dial oak-carved barometer, c. 1920.*

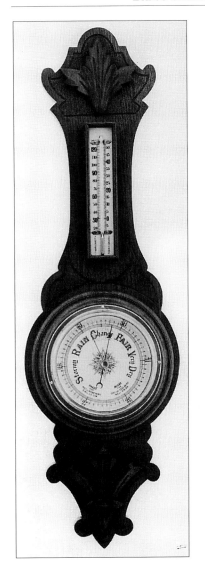 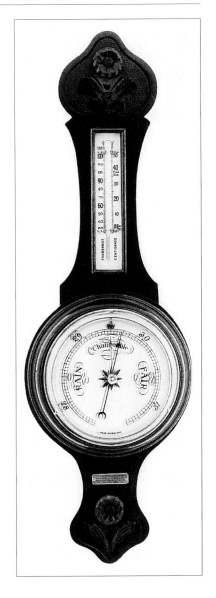

Left, Fig. 6.35: *Simple oak-carved case with 4.5 inch ceramic dial, c. 1925.*

Right, Fig. 6.36: *Dark oak barometer with 8 inch white glass dial, c. 1929.*

127

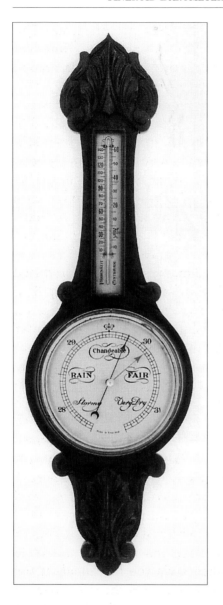 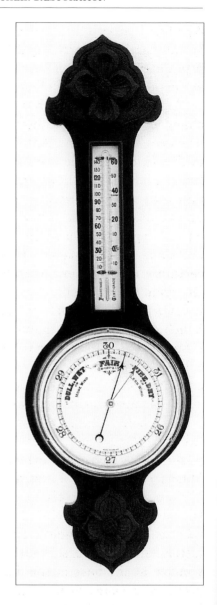

Left, Fig. 6.37: *An 8 inch printed dial on painted metal, Short & Mason style, c. 1929.*

Right, Fig. 6.38: *An 8 inch white glass dial oak barometer with different weather words, c. 1920.*

Jacobean to suit furniture that was popular at this time. The barometer featured in Fig. 6.40 shows more distinctly the transition into the 1930s. It is an 8 inch etched brass dial barometer in an oak banjo case, of carved and moulded design, circa 1930s.

This chapter should have demonstrated how gradually designs changed, particularly as manufacturing processes were simplified to produce cheaper items. Although better-quality barometers were still available, many of the mass-produced items would have probably been like the barometer shown in Fig. 6.41, an 8 inch electro silver-plated dial with an oak (probably imported not English oak) routered case and applied roundels of very simple design; even the dial now takes on the appearance of a reproduction dial, not a new design and not quite like the old patterns. Reproductions of earlier barometers were certainly nothing new: even Victorian makers sometimes produced Georgian design barometers but with aneroid movements. Fig. 6.42 illustrates a reproduction barometer by Short & Mason. It is an 8 inch white glass dial mahogany-cased barometer and thermometer of the 1930s. The case is a full-size mercury design of about 1870, but solid, with applied C-scroll carvings. Even the dial is divided with an expanded scale, and one would have to check on the back to make sure that this was an aneroid. Note the number of screws around the bezel to hold it down: partly the result of the engineering approach taken by the makers but also necessary because the dial has springs pushing up underneath to hold it firmly to the bezel. Another Short & Mason barometer is illustrated in Fig. 6.43, a 6 inch dial Short & Mason patent (original in 1932) indicating barometer and thermometer in simplified hexagonal pendant form with carved rosettes, the dial of acid-etched process with red and black coloured letters and numbers, weather forecasting instructions and little window at the base of the dial to indicate via the flag inside if the pressure is rising or falling. This is a very good rather under-rated barometer, even if the case does somewhat spoil its looks. For another design of case that is firmly rooted in the 1920–30 period, see the barometer illustrated in Fig. 6.44, a 6 inch brass dial oak-cased barometer and thermometer with barley-twist column supports and diamond lozenge stuck-on decoration around a hexagonal frame.

The interruption of the Second World War radically altered the production of barometer designs. Just after the end of the war some

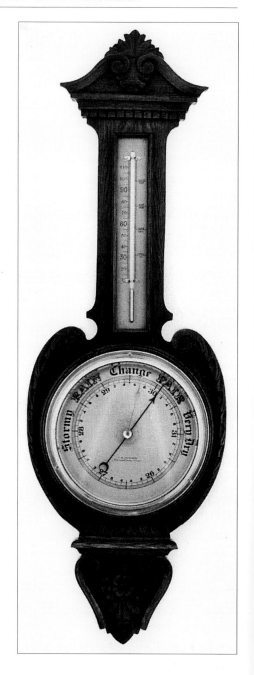

Left, Fig. 6.39: *Etched brass 8 inch dial barometer in heavy carved oak case, c. 1929.*

Right, Fig. 6.40: *Etched silvered brass 8 inch dial with all applied carving and mouldings, c. 1935.*

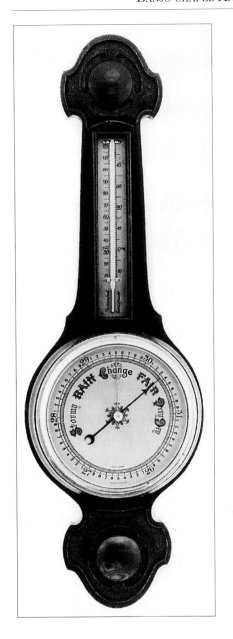

Left, Fig. 6.41: *Electro silver-plated 8 inch dial in routered oak case, c. 1935.*

Right, Fig. 6.42: *Electro silver-plated 8 inch dial reproduction barometer in mahogany case, c. 1930.*

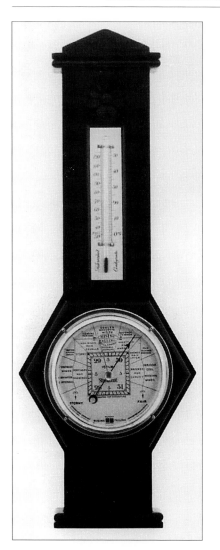

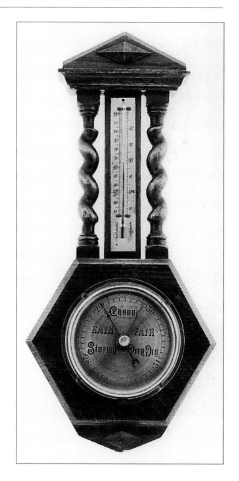

Left, Fig. 6.43: *A 6 inch Short & Mason 'Storm-o-Guide' barometer, c. 1932 onwards.*

Right, Fig. 6.44: *A 6 inch lacquered brass dial oak barometer with barley twists, c. 1930.*

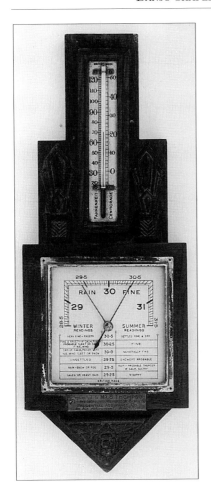

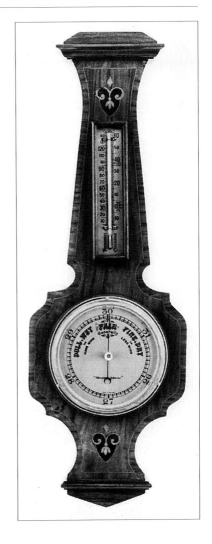

Left, Fig. 6.45: *A 6 inch square aluminium dial in oak case with pressed decoration applied, dated 1946.*

Right, Fig. 6.46: *Etched and silver-plated 6 inch dial walnut veneered and inlaid barometer, c. 1950.*

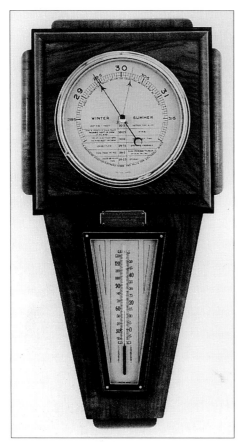

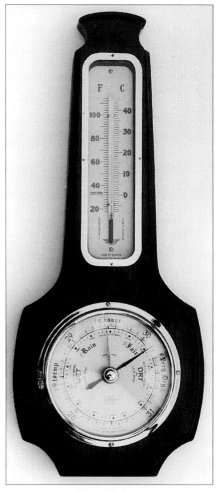

Left, Fig. 6.47: *Walnut veneered barometer with 8 inch aluminium dial, c. 1950.*

Right, Fig. 6.48: *A 3.5 inch aluminium dial barometer in an elm case, c. 1960.*

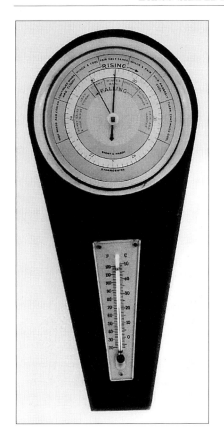

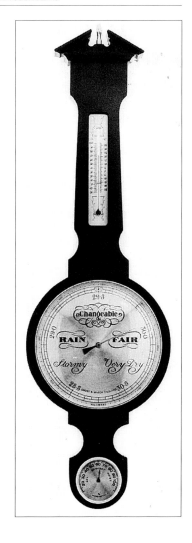

Left, Fig. 6.49: *A 4 inch aluminium dial barometer in mahogany case, c. 1960.*

Right, Fig. 6.50: *Modern reproduction barometer of the 1970s with 8 inch dial.*

pre-war designs were reintroduced, but new designs quickly took charge. The barometer shown in Fig. 6.45 is a 6 inch aluminium dial oak-cased barometer and thermometer, dated 1946, the bezel chromed and the case of simplified flatwood design – not a very elegant design but perhaps much admired by its owner. A somewhat more interesting style to collect is the type featured in Fig. 6.46, a 6 inch silvered acid-etched brass dial and thermometer scale pendant barometer, an elaborately cross-banded and inlaid item of good quality, circa 1950s. Normally, the movements underneath these dials are very standard mediocre small movements, whereas the slightly earlier varieties used the full-sized 4 inch base plate aneroid movements of earlier days. From the same period is the barometer illustrated in Fig. 6.47, an 8 inch aluminium dial walnut veneered barometer and thermometer of the 1950s with chrome bezel built on plywood base. This is quite typical of post-war furniture designs: remember the walnut veneered bedroom suites and wireless cases? It is a complete design on its own and does not even try to reproduce earlier styles of barometers. Fig. 6.48 is a 3.5 inch aluminium dial elm-cased barometer and thermometer of the 1960s by Shortland Instruments. The movements used in this style were often of extremely high quality, utilising all metal rack and pinion systems, probably just after the war but soon became more domestic in quality. Casework appears not to have been a priority in the design of the barometer shown in Fig. 6.49, which is a 4 inch aluminium dial mahogany-cased barometer and thermometer of early 1960s style by Short & Mason, described as a 'Storm-o-Guide' barometer with weather indications for rising and falling. Finally, Fig. 6.50 shows an example of an 8 inch aluminium dial barometer and thermometer of the 1970s by Short & Mason, with plastic or acrylic glass utilising the modern movement shown in Fig. 2.41. It is made of solid wood and retains some traditional designs of earlier barometers, but it comes as a poor conclusion to some of the high-quality instruments made by this fine company, especially in the pre-war years. However, one can hardly blame an individual manufacturer if good quality does not sell but the cheaper option makes a profit.

7 Other Wall Barometers

Having considered ship's and brass barometers, and having devoted a separate chapter to the banjo or pendant-style aneroid, this short chapter is generally concerned with round barometers with wooden cases. Naturally, the designs of these can vary only slightly, the movements and dials being almost identical to the banjo barometers of the periods they relate to, although numerous designs have been made, particularly in more recent decades, utilising square or angular pieces of wood to minimise the production costs of the case to hold the barometer movement. The main difference is generally in the decoration of the turned case. This can be done by carving and inlaying, and here there are a few variations which the reader will find of interest and may be able to find some examples. Among the best of these is shown in Fig. 7.1, a 10 inch hand-engraved silvered dial aneroid barometer in mahogany case by Samuel & Benjamin Solomons of 39 Albemarle Street, Piccadilly. This model, dating from the 1860s, is of high quality. Fig. 7.2 shows another very good-quality oak-cased aneroid wall barometer of around 1875 with carved laurel leaf decoration. The 8 inch dial is engraved silvered brass with the first letters of the weather words waxed in red, with the remainder in black wax. It is also fitted with a curved thermometer and the engraving is particularily fine with an unwaxed pattern in the centre. Utilising a card dial is the barometer shown in Fig. 7.3, an 8 inch printed dial ship's barometer with simulated carved rope design or pattern to the wooden case, the barometer mounted with a curved thermometer, dating from approximately 1875. As with the banjo-shaped barometers, 10 inch dials are quite scarce. Fig. 7.4 shows a 10 inch ceramic dial aneroid barometer by Joseph Somalvico & Co., circa 1880s, with curved thermometer, in a turned oak case. Note the unusual style of hand which is a tapered balance rather than the usual crescent. Dial sizes on these smaller barometers vary more than the banjo-shaped ones, perhaps to offer a greater selection in what

Above left, Fig. 7.1: *A 10 inch engraved silvered dial barometer by Samuel & Benjamin Solomons, c. 1865.*

Above right, Fig. 7.2: *Engraved silvered 8 inch dial barometer by Clerke with curved thermometer, c. 1875.*

Below left, Fig. 7.3: *An 8 inch card dial barometer with rope-carved effect edge, c. 1875.*

Below right, Fig. 7.4: *Turned barometer with 10 inch ceramic dial by Joseph Somalvico & Co., c. 1880.*

 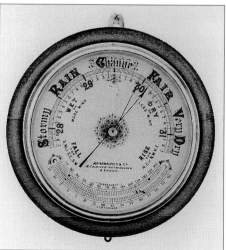

could be a rather limited variation of design. Fig. 7.5 shows a 7 inch ceramic dial aneroid barometer in octagonal turned and carved case with curved thermometer, circa 1885, inscribed Husbands of Bristol.

One of the main advantages of a barometer with a dial indicating the pressure is that the movement of the pointer is far in excess of the linear movement of a standard mercury tube barometer. Therefore, it is not surprising that efforts were made to make even greater use of the dial. When compared with the early Dent barometers, where there is a smaller movement than the later barometers, between 28 inches and 31 inches, the standard became 28–31 inches over half of the dial, i.e. six inches of mercury divided on the dial. It is perhaps surprising that fewer more sensitive barometers were not made such as Fig. 7.6, which illustrates a patent rapid indicating aneroid barometer in a carved oak case, with an 8 inch diameter silvered dial with black and red wax-filled characters and intricate pattern engraved design in the centre. The expansion of the dial is almost three inches of mercury, twice that of the normal barometer. This barometer probably dates from the late nineteenth century and is again by that well-known quality manufacturer of many other instruments, Chadburns Ltd, 47 Castle Street, Liverpoool. It will be seen from the detailed photograph of the mechanism in Fig. 7.7 that to obtain this considerable increase in magnification a second fulcrum point is used coming from the spring and screwed on to the base plate, thus magnifying the movement considerably. The metal arm from the spring is also temperature compensated, as it is made of steel. Because of the exaggerated movement, a spiral spindle is used to take up the extra movement of the fusee chain from the corresponding arm. You may notice the adaptation of the bracket retaining the fusee chain assembly by the cutting of a notch to allow the arm greater movement towards the spindle. The only other rapid indicating barometer I have managed to find is the one shown in Fig. 7.8, a 4.75 inch white glass dial oak-mounted barometer, circa 1890, with the patent 'Rapid Indicating' aneroid design. This is probably the same patent as the Chadburn barometer, but this one is inscribed C.S.S.A. Ltd, London, WC. I have been unable to ascertain the retailer or the manufacturer of this instrument, unless it was the Cooperative Science Supply.

The barometer illustrated in Fig. 7.9 is a very pleasant rope design oak-cased round barometer with 8 inch diameter ceramic dial. This

Above, Fig. 7.5: *A 7 inch ceramic dial in octagonal carved case, c. 1885.*

Below, Fig. 7.6: *An 8 inch engraved silvered dial, patented 'Rapid Indicating' barometer by Chadburns Ltd, c. 1890.*

Above, Fig. 7.7: *Close-up view of the mechanism of Chadburns' 'Rapid Indicating' barometer, c. 1890.*

Below, Fig. 7.8: *A 4.75 inch white glass dial patent 'Rapid Indicating' barometer, c. 1890.*

one was sold by Mappin & Webb, probably around 1890. A fascinating porcelain-mounted barometer by Negretti & Zambra is illustrated in Fig. 7.10, numbered 30396, with hand-engraved brass silvered dial, the bezel with gilt finish and hand decorated, probably imitation Royal Worcester, with ceramic mounting, measuring approximately 10 inches overall diameter, with a good-quality aneroid mechanism, screwed to a wooden block behind the bezel. From the style of the mechanism, I estimate this to be around the 1890s, which I think falls in line with the porcelain design. The dial is hand engraved, and rather crudely hand engraved, which indicates that this was possibly a one-off special for a customer, and it is the first one I have come across of this type. A barometer with a less appealing design is featured in Fig. 7.11, which shows a very late Victorian, perhaps around 1899, 'jelly mould' barometer. The decorative copper case is mounted on an oak-turned base with brass bezel and ceramic dial. The 'jelly mould' is purely a nickname by which this barometer became known in the workshop and does not have any real associations with identifying barometers!

Returning to another common design, Fig. 7.12 shows a 6 inch white glass dial ship's barometer of rope pattern design. The open lettering on the dial is a good indication for dating as well as the use of white glass and the poorer quality carved rope. Earlier barometers usually have much fine carving which shows the 'rope' in more detail; this example is probably around 1910. There are not many examples of small inlaid barometers like the one given in Fig. 7.13 which shows an 8 inch white glass dial aneroid barometer in ornately inlaid mahogany case of around 1910. The top panel is of flame mahogany inlaid and edged with boxwood and ebony; there is a fan inlay to base and floral inlays to side and top of the barometer: a very unusual and quite attractive barometer.

Moving on in time to after the First World War, there is generally a noticeable change in design; and while it is still quite possible to find a good-quality barometer, it will most likely be in a simple case like Fig. 7.14, a plywood and oak square aluminium dialled aneroid barometer, with square open panel, circa 1920. There is no bezel to hold the glass on, but four little corner mounts. The hand is of double-pointer style to give rising or falling predictions, and the whole design is perhaps of Art Deco influence. Aluminium gradually became the predominant material for barometer dials between the wars, especially

Above left, Fig. 7.9: *An 8 inch ceramic dial barometer with rope-carved effect edge, c. 1890.*

Above right, Fig. 7.10: *Negretti & Zambra porcelain barometer with 10 inch overall diameter, c. 1890.*

Below left, Fig. 7.11: *Ceramic 6 inch dial barometer mounted on oak and copper surround, c. 1899.*

Below right, Fig. 7.12: *White glass 6 inch dial barometer with rope-carved effect edge, c. 1910.*

Above, Fig. 7.13: *White glass 8 inch dial inlaid mahogany barometer, c. 1910.*

Below, Fig. 7.14: *A 4.25 inch aluminium square dial oak-veneered plywood barometer, c. 1920.*

on the less expensive ones, but there is a greater variety during this period when all the types of materials are compared. Fig. 7.15 shows another type of patented weather indicator by Benzie of Cowes, Isle of Wight, an 8 inch aluminium printed dial in carved rope traditional oak case of the 1930s. By moving the brass lever at the base of the barometer, one can turn the whole mechanism and therefore the black hand back to the setting point. However, since the dial is divided in inches it is difficult to ascertain why this should have been required, as it is not a travelling moving barometer, particularly as it has only one hanging. While it is probably true that the greatest number of barometers produced before the First World War were made by the eminent Victorian firm of Negretti & Zambra, between the wars, and indeed after, Short & Mason must have made the largest share of movements for the better-quality market. Fig. 7.16 depicts another Short & Mason barometer in octagonal mahogany case with ebony and boxwood inlay into the edge, of simple acid-etched dial design, from the 1930s. Fig. 7.17 illustrates a 1930s Short & Mason barometer with a dial of painted metal with printed design.

Fig. 7.18 shows a 6 inch open dial barometer by Dollond of London in carved decorated turned oak case, with traditional bezel and mechanism with a brass-etched dial, grained and lacquered (i.e. not silvered), dating from around the 1930s. A very common piece in its day is the brush set illustrated in Fig. 7.19, even now to be found among second-hand shops around the country. This hall brush set combination with barometer, dating from the 1930s, has a plywood and beech polished frame. The open 3.5 inch dial is of enamel with chromed bezel. While some collectors prefer to acquire only the best quality they can afford, often from a particular period, I find a great deal of fun in buying right across the range of barometers that have been produced. Good-quality barometers are often kept by a family or sold in auction. The less regarded barometers must often have been thrown away, which is perhaps why finding a barometer like the one illustrated in Fig. 7.20, a moulded bakelite-cased aneroid barometer by Short & Mason with a 4 inch printed dial, often at a very cheap price, is of interest to me and perhaps other readers. Note the centre knob. This model is an example of patent no. 589005, dated 1945 (see the Appendix), and was commonly in use into the 1960s. The brass or chrome setting hand is held in by a spring-loaded device which is

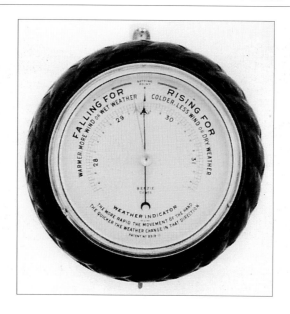

Above, Fig. 7.15: *Aluminium 8 inch dial patented barometer by Benzie of Cowes, c. 1930.*

Below, Fig. 7.16: *Etched silvered 4.75 inch dial barometer in line-inlaid mahogany case by Short & Mason, c. 1930.*

Above left, Fig. 7.17: *A 4.5 inch printed painted metal dial with visible movement by Short & Mason, c. 1930.*

Above right: Fig. 7.18: *Barometer with 6 inch brass dial in simple carved turned oak surround by Dollond, c. 1930.*

Below, Fig. 7.19: *Brush set and barometer with 3.5 inch enamel dial, c. 1935.*

first threaded through the hole in the glass (we usually pull them with a fine pair of pliers); the hand is located and twisted to $90°$ and then the spring-loaded metal is released to grip against the glass. Although this design is quite sensible in practical terms, after many years of wear the springs become stiff, the rubbers wear out and there is the cost of producing quite an elaborate affair. The traditional riveted brass knob and hand is so much more simple and can last for over a hundred years. This particular patented set-hand and knob requires about five different components, and possibly the cost alone forced it to disappear from the market. Another clue to the lateness of the manufacture of this barometer is the division of the dial. Note that there are four inches of mercury divided round the dial which is generally the more modern movement.

Fig. 7.21 shows an octagonal Short & Mason Storm-o-Guide, with 6 inch diameter dial, silvered acid-etched black and red filled engraving, with weather indications and 'flag' for rising or falling. Available before and after the Second World War, this one probably dates from about 1938. The reverse can be seen in Fig. 7.22, showing the patented altitude adjusting device. By rotating the dial, the entire movement turns, thus removing the need to tension the adjusting screw as with most traditional barometers.

The last rope-carved barometers were probably similar to the one shown in Fig. 7.23, a rather late rope-carved ship design aneroid barometer with acid-etched 8 inch dial and curved thermometer by John Barker & Co. Ltd, inscribed 'Marine Aneroid' from the 1960s. Surprisingly, the barometer in Fig. 7.24 is the only example of a 'ship's wheel' style that I have found. Many sea-side resorts sold these types in the 1950s and 1960s. This one is an elm-mounted barometer with brass spokes by Shortland Smiths Instruments, from the 1950s. These movements were often sold, as many are today, and mounted in various ways by wood turners. The use of elm indicates a possible wood-turning craft application. Interestingly, the movement in this barometer, being of the quadrant rack and pinion type, still manufactured after the war, is among the most accurate of these barometers. I have known some of these cheap-looking instruments to move exceptionally well when tested in the pressure chamber. The 'upside-down' look of Fig. 7.25 is quite eye-catching: it is a 6 inch aluminium dial aneroid barometer in unusual oak case, probably by O.C. Comitti, of the 1960s.

 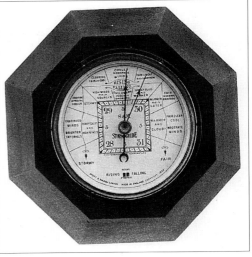

Above left, Fig. 7.20: *Printed aluminium 4 inch dial bakelite barometer by Short & Mason, c. 1946.*

Above right, Fig. 7.21: *A 6 inch etched silvered dial 'Storm-o-Guide' barometer by Short & Mason, c. 1938.*

Below, Fig. 7.22: *Reverse view of Fig. 7.21 showing altitude adjustment disc.*

Above left, Fig. 7.23: *Etched silvered 8 inch dial barometer with rope-effect edge, c. 1960.*

Above right, Fig. 7.24: *A 3.5 inch aluminium dial 'ship's wheel' style barometer in elm surround, c. 1955.*

Below, Fig. 7.25: *Oak-cased barometer with 6 inch aluminium dial by O. C. Comitti, c. 1965.*

Above: White flash glass 6 inch dial barometer in finely executed carved case of acorns and oak leaves with curved thermometer by Negretti & Zambra, c. 1885.

Below: Carved and turned German barometer with 5.25 inch dial printed on reverse of the front glass, c. 1910.

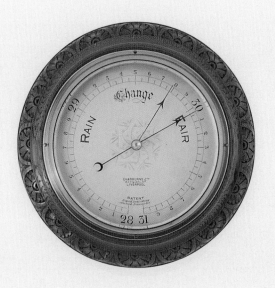

Above: Patented rapid indicating barometer with an 8 inch engraved silvered dial by Chadburns Ltd, c. 1890.

Below: Porcelain mounted 4.75 inch ceramic dial wall barometer inscribed J.S. Arthurs, 14 Brigg Street, Northampton, c. 1885.

Above, Fig. 7.26: *Oak-cased barometer with 6 inch aluminium dial, thermometer and storm glass, c. 1965.*

Below, Fig. 7.27: *Owl carved barometer with 3.75 inch enamel dial, c. 1960.*

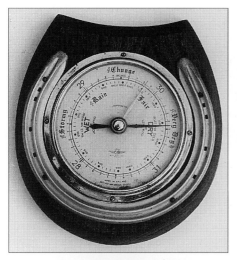

Above left, Fig. 7.28:
A 3.75 inch aluminium dial barometer in elm, with aluminium horseshoe nailed on, c. 1962.

Above right, Fig. 7.29:
A 2.75 inch aluminium dial barometer inserted into serpentine stone, c. 1965.

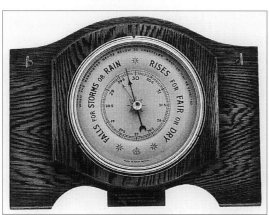

Centre right, Fig. 7.30:
Barometer with 4 inch aluminium dial inserted into blue and white Wedgwood plaque, c. 1969.

Bottom right, Fig. 7.31:
Aluminium 6 inch dial oak-mounted barometer with hooks for brushes, dated 1970.

From the same period is Fig. 7.26, a 6 inch aluminium dial aneroid barometer with thermometer and storm glass. The storm glass is usually associated with earlier mercury barometers named after Admiral Fitzroy and was often sold as a separate item in Victorian times. It is interesting to note its reappearance on this barometer; you may well find other examples.

The barometer in Fig. 7.27, a 1960s 'owl' barometer, shows a typical use for insert movements by some busy wood-carving establishment, possibly for sale to tourists. The style of carving insinuates that this was possibly made in Germany and is similar to the Black Forest carvings of later cuckoo clocks, but the origins are unknown. Also very common in the 1960s was the horseshoe design barometer shown in Fig. 7.28, an elm horseshoe barometer with 3.75 inch dial by Shortland Smiths Instruments, around 1962.

Visitors to The Lizard in Cornwall over the years, at least since the Second World War, have been able to purchase numerous decorative items from craftsmen, often working in small sheds, who collect the natural serpentine stone which is often greenish with different marbling effects but can vary in colour, the scarcer stones being the more expensive. These craftsmen make many varied items from the stone, usually on lathes. Fig. 7.29 shows one of many types of serpentine stone aneroid barometers, from the 1960s, the insert barometer by Smiths utilising a rack and pinion movement of fine quality. Many later ones have very ordinary movements.

As a change from inserting clocks into items, barometers have often been used. Even the famous firm of Wedgwood produce a wall plaque with a barometer, as can be seen in Fig. 7.30. The insert movement is by Short & Mason with their latest 'Storm-o-Guide' dial, the glass held in position with three brass clips bolting through the decorative wall plaque. Finally, Fig. 7.31 shows a 6 inch aluminium printed dial oak-mounted wall barometer by O.C. Comitti, possibly for brushes (note the hooks to left and right of the dial). This one, with presentation plaque, dates from the 1970s.

Above, Fig. 8.1: *Engraved silvered 4.25 inch dial ship's wheel pattern barometer, dated 1857.*
Below, Fig. 8.2: *A 4.5 inch card dial barometer in brass case on walnut stand by Negretti & Zambra, c. 1863.*

8 Shelf, Table and Desk Barometers

Traditional mercury barometers were generally designed to hang on the wall, and, being approximately 3 ft long, this was usually the best place for them. Although the famous Quare barometers and similar styles were made as floor-standing models as well, they are definitely in the minority. Delicate mercury instruments sitting on the floor were not generally a common feature. However, with the development of the aneroid barometer along came new possibilities. The earliest free-standing barometers were generally brass-cased barometers of the 4.5 inch diameter style, normally sold with stands, usually made of carved wood. But other types were made such as the one shown in Fig. 8.1 which is a particularly nice example of Victorian extravagance. The metal case is gilded and stands on an ebony veneered base. The movement and dial are very similar to the Dent design but of higher-quality engineering. It is engraved May 1857 and was presented, one imagines, to a sea-going person. To move the brass hand you actually turn the ship's wheel which is connected to the brass bezel and the hand is fixed in position on the glass which all turns together. One can perhaps imagine that some veteran sea captain set his desk barometer every morning with due ceremony!

The next two barometers illustrated are rested loosely on their stands which could have been sold as an extra to many different barometers. Fig. 8.2 is a 4.5 inch cardboard dial brass-cased aneroid barometer by Negretti & Zambra, around 1863, on associated carved walnut stand in original polish. This is a very fine example of an early aneroid barometer by Negretti & Zambra, their name printed in script with 'Opticians to Her Majesty' and their various business addresses in London. The barometer in Fig. 8.3 is an 8 inch open card dial aneroid barometer on associated carved oak stand by Cox & Coombes of Devonport, possibly the retailers, awarded as a prize for

155

HMS *Britannia,* around 1870. Soft metal as well as bronze stands were available such as the prancing stallion shown in Fig. 8.4, with a simple 4.5 inch dial brass-cased barometer held within a curved metal support, easily detachable, the weight of the barometer in this instance creating considerable strain on the upright supports. These have often been found to be damaged due to this inherent design problem. The slightly stronger design of stand shown in Fig. 8.5 incorporates a pair of cherubs mounted on an ebonized wood stand, supporting another 6 inch dial aneroid barometer with open mechanism, around 1875. When the aneroid barometer truly began to get into its stride and varied from the 4.5 inch dial brass case, then a whole profusion of unusual cases and combinations resulted.

A very rare aneroid barometer is illustrated in Fig. 8.6, a Watkins patent 'snail' divided dial c.1886, with 4.5 inch diameter brass case showing brass 'feet' at back making this into a standing or hanging barometer. The movement incorporates one of the patented Watkins designs manufactured by Watson & Sons, London, the hand extending further as it reaches higher pressure and becoming shorter as it ascends higher and obtains less air pressure, by utilising a cord fitted around a brass wheel. This almost Heath Robinson affair is not very satisfactory. The extra friction involved makes it extremely difficult to work (see the Appendix for patent nos 3425 and 14730 of 1886).

There were many combination clock and barometers made, often with a thermometer between them. Fig. 8.7 shows one such item, a late Victorian carved oak combination piece, with clock, thermometer and barometer, printed card dials of 4 inch diameter, made around 1890. Another later model is shown in Fig. 8.8, an Edwardian continental clock, thermometer and barometer combination piece in veneered walnut, with enamelled 3.5 inch dials to clock and barometer and silvered brass thermometer scale to centre.

The addition of small brass feet seems quite common on medium to small brass-cased barometers, making wider use of the cases at very little extra cost. Fig. 8.9 shows a 3 inch diameter brass-cased barometer with two short front legs to allow easy standing. The mechanism, probably continental, is of the rack and pinion design. Note the Bourdon-style setting hand (referring to the hollow or fretted centre), a further suggestion that this is a French barometer, of around 1900.

Above, Fig. 8.3:
An 8 inch open card dial barometer by Cox & Coombes on oak stand, c. 1870.

Left, Fig. 8.4:
A 4.5 inch card dial barometer held by prancing stallion, c. 1875.

Above left, Fig. 8.5: *Engraved silvered open 6 inch dial barometer held by* putti, *c. 1875.*
Above right, Fig. 8.6: *Engraved silvered 'snail' 4.5 inch dial Watkins patent barometer, c. 1886.*

Below, Fig. 8.7: Clock, thermometer and barometer with 4 inch card dial in oak stand, c. 1890.

Above, Fig. 8.8: *A 3.5 inch enamel dial clock, barometer and thermometer, c. 1910.*

Below, Fig. 8.9: *Brass-cased barometer with 3 inch card dial, c. 1900.*

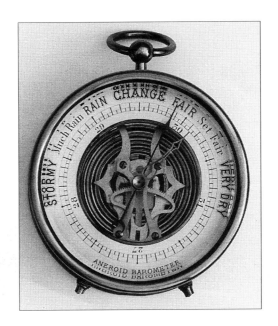

Silversmiths have lent their talents to many different designs in housing barometers. Fig. 8.10 is an interesting silver-mounted pocket watch barometer with enamel dial of about 1905. Numerous items such as these were made and sold, often with very thin silver casings. This one is of particularly good-quality heavy silver, but is naturally hollow. The barometers are normally of no special merit and are invariably adapted from barometers which were regularly made at the time. Weathercraft is the name inscribed on the very typical Art Deco-style acrylic barometer seen in Fig. 8.11. Interestingly, it utilises an altimeter movement that was available in the 1930s, which suggests to me that the movements were bought direct from factories producing altimeters for aircraft and mounted in this unusual design. The hands are of lightweight aluminium, and I cannot help thinking that this design is similar to a wireless of the period. The barometer illustrated in Fig. 8.12 is an 11 inch dial Storm-o-Guide, shop display model from Gorleston-on-Sea made by Short & Mason. The mechanism can be set for altitude from the reverse by revolving the patent dial, the Storm-o-Guide relating to the small window underneath the hand between numbers 27 and 26 which reveals a flag, which moves left or right according to whether the barometer is falling or rising. This is operated by a simple clutch mechanism and is a particular trade mark of Short & Mason. This particular design is in American walnut and was presumably offered to jewellers and opticians for shop display, advertising, and so on. The copyright on this patent is 1930 which indicates that this barometer dates from then onwards. I have seen smaller designs into the 1950s; this one probably dates from the mid-1930s.

There are two particular German desk barometers that an avid collector should eventually find. One is illustrated in Fig. 8.13, the Zeiss table barometer of about 1935. The original purchase price of this in 1937 would have been £3 3s. However, I cannot agree with some of the advertising literature, particularly the numbers and divisions appearing to be needle sharp seen against a frosted glass background. Depending on the lighting this may be so, but generally it can be quite difficult to read some of these barometers, especially now that they are beginning to deteriorate and the printing is coming away or fading from the glass. None the less, this barometer makes an intriguing collector's piece. I have recently bought one at a very

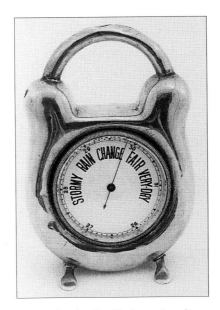

Above, Fig. 8.10: *Enamel 2 inch dial pocket barometer housed in a silver lock, c. 1905.*

Below, Fig. 8.11: *Art Deco acrylic-cased barometer with aluminium dial, c. 1930s.*

reasonable price, although one cannot guarantee that they are working and they suffer the usual problems with bellows. The second one to look out for is pictured in Fig. 8.14 by G.P. Goerz of Berlin. The mechanism is cleverly hidden within the base of the barometer and the fusee chain connection goes to the centre of the glass dial. The dial is printed in English, although the substitution of 'Uncertain' for the word 'Change' makes a particularly curious variation. The base of the barometer, on dismantling, reveals the mechanism described in patent no. 227312, dated 1924. The barometer illustrated here is thought to be soon after that date, although mounted differently for the fusee chain movement is vertically above the diaphragm instead of horizontal with it.

Returning to British-made barometers, Fig. 8.15 is an unusual Short & Mason bakelite or plastic-moulded case simulating a figured wood, this particular model with approximately a 3.5 inch dial, dating from the 1930s. Bakelite seems to have been a choice of material used for cases for a very limited period only. Perhaps it was a material that customers thought inferior after a history of wood and brass cases on barometers. I suspect today it would be a preferable choice to the compressed fibreboard (MDF) with printed grain applied that appears in some outlets. The Storm-o-Guide barometer in red painted bakelite case by Short & Mason shown in Fig. 8.16 is certainly more appealing. The bezel on this is a tight push fit over the bakelite and, with age, is extremely difficult to remove. This is an interesting use of material for a desk barometer.

I have evidence that the barometer shown in Fig. 8.17, a mahogany-mounted desk barometer with 6 inch etched silvered dial, by Short & Mason, was sold in the late 1950s, but believe that they were first made in the 1930s. It is almost impossible to tell pre-war and post-war models apart, but they are often marked inside by the assembler with a date. The polished case with black edges to exaggerate the stepped design of the case utilises the good-quality movement associated with Short & Mason. Proof that the aviation industry converted to barometer manufacture is shown by the example illustrated in Fig. 8.18, which is a particular favourite of mine. Almost certainly manufactured by Field Aircraft Instruments and Equipment Limited of Willow Lane, Mitcham Junction, Surrey (see patent no. 588890 in the Appendix, the application dated 9th March 1945 and

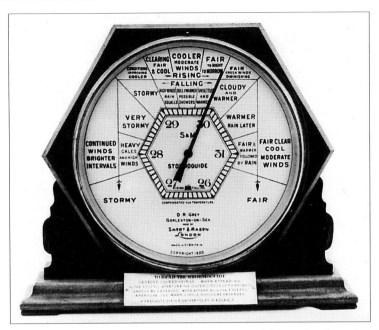

Above, Fig. 8.12: *Shop display barometer with 11 inch etched silvered dial in American walnut case, c. 1935.*
Below left, Fig. 8.13: *Chromium-plated barometer by Zeiss, c. 1935.*
Below right, Fig. 8.14: *Blackened brass-cased barometer with 3.5 inch glass dial by G.P. Goerz of Berlin, c. 1925.*

Above, Fig. 8.15: *Bakelite imitation walnut barometer with 3.5 inch printed aluminium dial, c. 1938.*

Below, Fig. 8.16: *Storm-o-Guide barometer with 4.25 inch etched silvered dial by Short & Mason, c. 1935.*

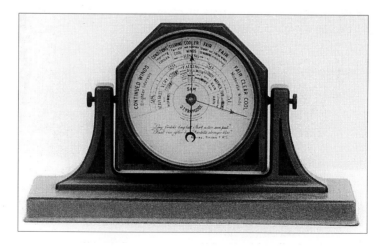

Above, Fig. 8.17: *Etched silvered 6 inch dial barometer in mahogany case by Short & Mason, c. 1937.*

Below, Fig. 8.18: *Cast aluminium case desk set with rotating printed dials, c. 1945.*

complete specification accepted 5th June 1947), this shows the winding down of the war effort and diversification to make domestic items, the design of this particular barometer being the object then to provide a new and attractive type of aneroid barometer. Made in a cast aluminium case with added chrome-plated parts, it indicates air pressure with a pictorial representation of expected weather at certain pressures, i.e. sunshine at high pressure changing gradually to cloudy and then more rain and heavy rain at low pressure in one continuous revolving picture. Above the pressure reading is a revolving temperature dial. Below the pressure dial is a recessed rotating ring marked in inches of mercury; there is a small stud projecting to enable it to be manually turned to line up with a mark to allow recording of the pressure. I have found few of these surviving so assume that they were either not successful or the costs of production were too great. Certainly the quality of the item is far in excess of anything one usually finds made a few years after the Second World War, but it is common to find that during the late 1940s and early 1950s Britain was still producing high-quality barometers, presumably because of an established engineering background. It is sad to relate that soon afterwards, in the late 1950s and 1960s, much mass production was introduced and, as a generalisation, the quality of instruments for the domestic market fell significantly.

Another barometer which uses this design of dial is pictured in Fig. 8.19. Judging by the quality of the movement inside the barometer, it was probably made by Short & Mason. It is a desk barometer with chrome casing on a mahogany base, the mechanism a Short & Mason type, the rack and pinion with beryllium copper capsules, dating from the 1950s. The dial is formed at right angles down the side, the needle extending also down the side, to read from the top but also sideways through cut-out slots in the casing. Similar to the design of the barometer in Fig. 8.16 is the barometer illustrated in Fig. 8.20, with a 5 inch printed aluminium dial and chrome bezel with summer and winter predictions on the lower half of the dial, this time in a primitive oak frame by O.C. Comitti made during the late 1960s. The use of brass in the desk barometer of Fig. 8.21 makes a change from all the examples made of more recent materials. The dial is 2.25 inches in diameter acid etched (processed) and silvered, within a spun brass stand. In addition to the examples illustrated of barometers of post-

Above, Fig. 8.19: *A 3 inch formed dial printed on painted metal with chromed case on mahogany base, c. 1955.*

Below, Fig. 8.20: *Oak-framed barometer with 5 inch printed aluminium dial by O.C. Comitti, c. 1969.*

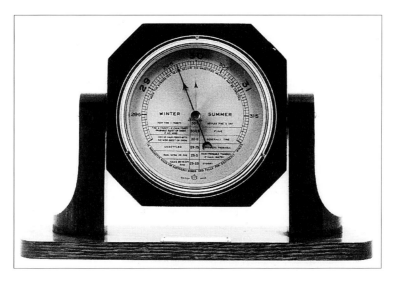

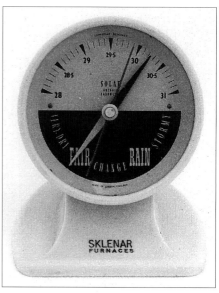

Above left, Fig. 8.21:
Etched silvered 2.25 inch dial brass-cased barometer, c. 1959.

Above right, Fig. 8.22:
Printed 3 inch dial plastic-cased 'trade' barometer, 1966.

Left, Fig. 8.23:
A peculiar barometer, hygrometer and thermometer inspired by Sputnik, c. 1965.

168

war Britain, there were also a number of brass-cased models made especially for the marine industry, but they generally utilise designs of earlier years and do not much reflect the influence of styles in vogue after the war. For this reason they are also very difficult to date.

Barometers advertising businesses have been made during the last half of this century. Perhaps the most well known is the 'Guinness' barometer made in large numbers in the 1960s, often with the logo 'A fine day for Guinness' printed on them, usually in plain wood cases or pressed anodised aluminium cases. The quality of most of these items is usually, of necessity, poor: few firms want to give away expensive gifts; the idea is to promote firms and even the cheaper types of barometer can be regarded as more expensive than many other promotional items, particularly when special dials are printed. The barometer shown in Fig. 8.22 is a plastic-cased barometer made for Sklenar Furnaces in the 1960s. These barometers seldom generate much interest among collectors, from the aspect of mechanism or quality, but they have a certain charm in their individual designs, which quite often would only have been made in relatively small numbers, compared with the mass market of the domestic barometer through the usual outlets. Finally in this chapter, marking perhaps the dawn of a new age, is the 1960s 'Sputnik' barometer featured in Fig. 8.23.

9 Continental Barometers

While the majority of barometers purchased in Britain over the last century were made in Britain, a tremendous number were imported from Europe, Germany being among the largest producer. I have always thought their high quality of engineering to be the predominant factor in this. It is slightly ironic to find a Darton advertisement of around 1910 for cheap foreign aneroid barometers – somewhat knocking the imported barometers as of inferior quality – and now to see, some 80 and 90 years later, those same cheap foreign aneroid barometers surviving on the whole far better than their English counterparts. Although the English barometers were made to good quality, the wood used was often oak and, having tannin in it, this created some problems with the mechanisms. German movements, being made predominantly of brass and well lacquered in fruitwood or semi-hardwood cases, often still look remarkably good and work very well when tested in a pressure chamber. I suspect that the cheapness of price enjoyed during the Edwardian period helped to endorse people's opinions of 'foreign imports'.

While the original intention of this book was to trace the development of the aneroid barometer in Britain, I believe it would not be complete without the inclusion of some barometers from the continent and particularly German barometers. These were imported in large numbers and have blended themselves in so well that they are generally regarded by most people as English barometers. I have already included a few continental barometers in this book; this chapter is to help recognise other continental designs, some of which are 'foreign' to the British style. The main determining factor is usually the style of bezel: the English bezel being of ogee design or thumbnail moulded design, incorporating a usually silvered reflecting ring sitting tight against the dial and often holding the dial in position; whereas German aneroid barometers usually have a thin right-angled bezel. Because of difficulty in replacing them, I have had four different sizes made to cater for the growing demand in replacement parts for this type of instrument.

Continental barometer manufacturers often used trade marks on their barometers, whereas British manufacturers often did not. The following examples may help in identifying some barometers. A considerable number of early brass barometers were of French manufacture often by a firm who used the founding directors' initials inside a circle P.H.N.B., as can be seen in Fig. 9.1. The firm was founded in 1860 and a firm still survives that uses these initials. Fig. 9.2 depicts the trade mark of L. Maxant, another mid-Victorian firm still trading today, and Fig. 9.3 shows the trade mark of Emil Scholz of Hamburg, Germany. Many of the enamel dial barometers have this mark on them, usually on the metal plate behind the mechanism (against the wall). There were many other companies but few marked their goods and so cannot be attributed to a particular maker.

Fig. 9.4 shows a highly elaborately carved 'goat' barometer from possibly around 1890, with oak leaves and acorns adorning the case. The movement is actually of slightly different design but of the Vidi-type movement; the 6 inch diameter dial, quite common on European barometers, is of printed card. Fig. 9.5 illustrates an open 3.5 inch card dial barometer with silvered engraved thermometer above the carved appearance of the case, actually made in two halves and joined, the material being a moulded resin of some type. I have heard of some types of barometer like this that were made from pig's blood and wood (an early type of chipboard)! Fig. 9.6 is of a carved and pierced case barometer with 4 inch diameter open dial, printed card and white glass thermometer scale, dated circa 1895. The case is carved with sticks and leaves in a 'rustic' design. It is quite common on these barometers to find that the bezel does not fit particularly well on the carved wood. This may be due to the fact that these barometers were made by out-workers: carvers worked during the winter months making barometer cases, and other items, for factories, and when they were assembled they found, perhaps, that some were not quite of the right size. It certainly endorses the fact that the carvers were separate from the barometer manufacturers. I feel sure that if a carver had bought the movements, then he would have carved the case to suit; whereas, if this process were done apart from the movement, and the movements changed or the measurements were not given

Above left, Fig. 9.1: *French trade mark using initials of founders of early barometer company, started 1860.*

Above right, Fig. 9.2: *Trade mark of L. Maxant, another Victorian French firm.*

Below, Fig. 9.3: *Trade mark of Emil Scholz, a German firm from about 1910.*

Left, Fig. 9.4: *A 6 inch card dial barometer in heavily carved fruitwood case, c. 1890.*

Right, Fig. 9.5: *A 3.5 inch card dial barometer with silvered engraved thermometer scale in moulded case, c. 1890.*

accurately, then you could easily get a slight discrepancy. The difference is usually only in the region of 0.125 inch and is not common as such, but happens frequently enough to be worth further consideration of the cause.

Perhaps the most commonly found continental barometer is that featured in Fig 9.7, a traditional Edwardian design barometer with open dial, made of cream enamel but sometimes of card and with a white glass thermometer scale. The thermometer scale slides down between the pillars, which are slotted to receive it, and the top semi-circular carving is screwed to the top of the pillars on the reverse. A common feature of these European barometers is the hanging plate. When looked at from the reverse it is a right-angled piece of steel positioned over a hole in the wood. Note the slenderness of design of the turnings to this barometer which dates from about 1910. As so many similar designs were imported, it is impossible to give accurate dates but only generalisations from the style and lettering involved: one has to develop a 'feeling' for the date of them. As a rough guide, the earlier ones seem to be finely carved and better quality, whereas later ones begin to lose the fine carving and turnings begin to be simpler. The modern equivalent is very similar in basic design but the turnings are mere knobs and the thermometer is screwed to a piece of wood between the pillars. I have found several catalogues of continental barometers which were available for importing around the beginning of the twentieth century. They could also be produced with weather words in other languages, and I have come across many barometers which I believe to have been made originally in Germany with Dutch and French weather indications.

The barometer illustrated in Fig. 9.8 has a possible Art Nouveau influence. It is an open-fretted and carved barometer with 3.5 inch open card dial of silvered effect, and thermometer scale of white glass, dating from around 1905. Identical turned surrounds, as used in barometers such as the one shown in Fig. 9.7, were made in a simple round form without pillars and finials. Fig. 9.9 shows a very typical one: the turned case is carved utilising the shapes of the turning, a typical feature of these barometers, with an open enamelled dial, from about 1910. There are many hundreds of these still available and on the market, generally at very low prices. More unusual to find, but still possible, is the variety that has more defined carving, as seen in

Left, Fig. 9.6: *A 4 inch card dial barometer with white glass thermometer in carved and pierced case, c. 1895.*

Right, Fig. 9.7: *Enamel 4.5 inch dial barometer, with thermometer scale of white glass, c. 1910.*

Above left, Fig. 9.8: *A 3.5 inch card dial open fretwork cased barometer, c. 1905.*

Above right: Fig. 9.9: *Enamel 4.25 inch dial turned and carved barometer, c. 1910.*

Below, Fig. 9.10: *Enamel 4.25 inch dial turned and carved acorn leaf barometer, c. 1910.*

Fig. 9.10. This shows a fine example of a 4.5 inch open enamel dial carved barometer, with finely executed carvings of acorns and oak leaves.

Not all continental barometers had card or enamel dials, although most did. Fig. 9.11 illustrates a turned and carved barometer with 4.25 inch dial, printed on the reverse of the glass, with chromed bezel, now disintegrating and the glass is cracked. Replacement glasses for these items have usually to be made to order and are normally cost-prohibitive for restoration. Carved barometers were far less popular on the British market: the finely carved 'sunflower' barometer in Fig. 9.12 has a white glass scale thermometer marked in Reaumur and Centigrade and a 3 inch open card dial of about the 1920s. The Art Nouveau influence is perhaps revealed in Fig. 9.13, a turned wooden case barometer, veneered and inlaid with coloured woods, typical of around 1900. I cannot be certain that the barometer in Fig. 9.14 is not of British manufacture, but it does not feel as though it is. It is different in that it has a white glass dial of about 1920 which might be British but the continental bezel and carved case look very much European in origin. A very good little barometer brought in for repair some years ago is pictured in Fig. 9.15, a 3.5 inch dial miniature barometer with open dial, cardboard scales. It is only approximately 14 inches long but is clearly modelled on an English mercury barometer of an earlier period; this one is in rosewood and of nice quality, made for an English retailer and possibly dating from around 1895.

Another noticeable difference between British and continental barometers is the way in which the thermometer is fitted to the case. Most times, British thermometers are fitted into a small oblong case with a glass front which is either held on to the barometer by keyhole slots and screws or recessed into the case and glued into position. I have noticed that most continental barometers are fitted with thermometers that are held into an opening in the barometer case from behind the barometer, thus creating a frame for the thermometer that is exposed to the elements. Fig. 9.16 is one such barometer, with white glass thermometer. Thermometers mounted like this, this one with a spiral thermometer, often suffer from dirt and breakage, being unprotected, the black figured lettering often fading to a light brown. A more commonly found case is the one shown in Fig. 9.17, being an

Above, Fig. 9.11: *A 4.25 inch reverse printed clear glass dial turned barometer, c. 1915.*

Centre, Fig. 9.12: *'Sunflower' carved barometer with 3 inch card dial, c. 1920.*

Below, Fig. 9.13: *Veneered and inlaid barometer with 3.25 inch dial, c. 1900.*

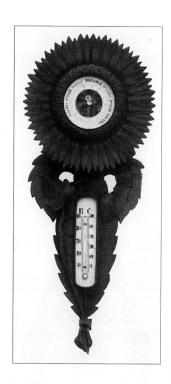

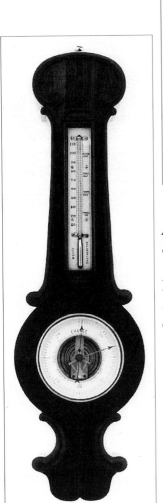

Above, Fig. 9.14: *White glass 3.5 inch dial barometer, c. 1920.*

Left, Fig. 9.15: *A 3.5 inch card dial miniature barometer in rosewood veneer, c. 1895.*

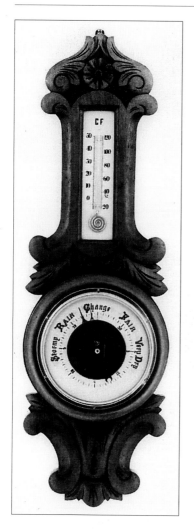

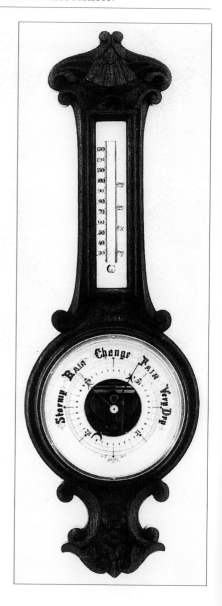

Left, Fig. 9.16: *An 8 inch enamel dial barometer with framed thermometer, c. 1900.*

Right: Fig. 9.17: *An 8 inch enamel dial barometer in common-style case, c. 1910.*

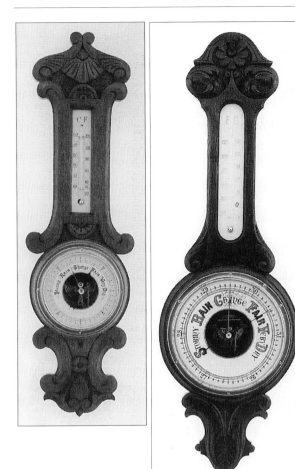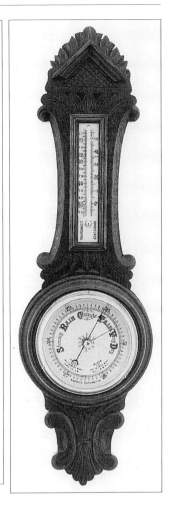

Left, Fig. 9.18: *Enamel 5.25 inch dial barometer, c. 1920.*

Centre, Fig. 9.19: *Enamel 8 inch dial barometer in oak case, c. 1930.*

Right, Fig. 9.20: *White glass 4.5 inch dial barometer in oak-carved case, c. 1920.*

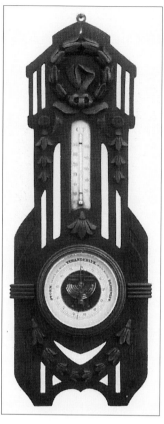

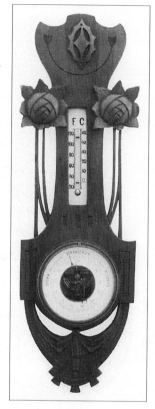

Left, Fig. 9.21:
A 4.5 inch card dial barometer in fretted and applied carving case, c. 1930.

Right, Fig. 9.22:
A 4.5 inch card dial barometer with plastic front, c. 1950.

8 inch open enamel dial in carved oak case of around 1910. These last two barometers both have 8 inch dials; other sizes are also commonly found, such as the barometer shown in Fig. 9.18, with 5.25 inch dial and slightly less proportioned case for the size of dial. Another case design sometimes found is featured in Fig. 9.19, a carved oak-cased aneroid barometer with 8 inch enamel open dial and white glass thermometer scale recessed from the back. This barometer is interesting in that it has a very small movement beneath the dial, which, being original, was probably a more economic model. Although perfectly operational, one would expect to find a full-size 4 inch mechanism underneath these dials. The slightly more British-looking barometer in Fig. 9.20 is a 1920s white glass dial and thermometer scale small barometer of about 19 inches in height, a typical design of the time. The thermometer scale is behind moulded framing, and the dial is approximately 4.5 inches. Note the cross-hatched carving

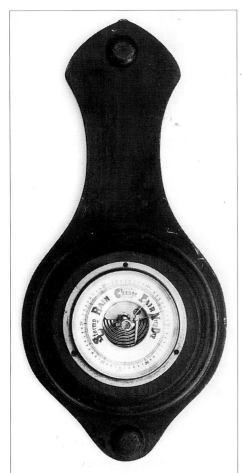

Fig. 9.23: *A 3.5 inch enamel dial barometer in very simple form, c. 1936.*

underneath the pseudo pediment: English barometers do not usually have this design carved on them. It is unusual for continental manufacturers to include their name, although I have noticed on some of the earlier ones the unicorn symbol of the Emil Scholz factory, and occasionally some more modern barometers have the name Lufft stamped into the back of the mechanism. The majority of continental barometers also lack the retailer's name, unlike many of British manufacture.

Designs also changed on the continent (as in Britain) to produce cheaper items. The simple barometer in Fig. 9.21 shows us an applied carving and fretted American walnut barometer with open card dial and white glass thermometer of the 1930s. The very finely cut edges (or stems of the flowers) in Fig. 9.22 are on a 4.5 inch open card dial barometer with chromed bezel and plastic front, with a thermometer scale of white glass, possibly from the 1950s, but even this is superior to the plywood-cased barometer of 1936 featured in Fig. 9.23 which has a 3.5 inch open enamel dial and applied roundels.

10 Bourdon Barometers

These barometers are another design of 'without liquid' barometer, named after their originator, Eugene Bourdon (1808–84), a French inventor and engineer. He generally had little success with barometers of this type but continued to design and make pressure gauges, still made today with Bourdon tubes, and very successfully. The Bourdon barometers that I have come across are a pleasure to behold. Compared with the normal Vidi barometer, Bourdons are a far superior piece of workmanship, comprising a very finely cut arched rack and pinion and balanced lever system. Particularly intriguing is the device to adjust the reading by insertion of a special key into the centre of the barometer from the back; the body of the key lifts a lever which brings down a tiny V-shaped metal piece like an axe which thus locks the pinion in position. Turning the key then turns the steel spindle holding the hand to the desired position. It slips within its fixing on the brass pinion. Removal of the key frees the pinion again which is a tight fit on to the centre spindle, thus adjusting the reading without moving the position of the levers, or the position of the rack or ends of the Bourdon tubes. Here is a description of the metallic or Bourdon tube from *A Treatise on Meteorological Instruments* published by Negretti & Zambra in 1864:

> This instrument, the invention of M. Bourdon, has a great resemblance to the aneroid, but is much simpler in arrangement. The inventor has applied the same principle to the construction of metallic steam-pressure gauges. We are here, however, only concerned with it as constructed to indicate atmospheric pressure. It consists of a long slender flattened metallic tube, partially exhausted of air, and hermetically closed at each end, then fixed upon its centre, and bent round so as to make the ends face each other. The transverse section of this tube is an elongated ellipse. The principle of action is this: interior pressure tends to straighten the tube, external pressure causes

it to coil more. Hence as the atmospheric pressure decreases, the ends of the tube become more apart.

This movement is augmented and transferred by a mechanical arrangement of small metallic levers to a radius bar, which carries a rack formed on the arc of its circle. This moves a pinion, upon the arbour of which a light pointer, or 'hand', is poised, which indicates the pressure upon a dial. When the pressure increases, the ends of the tube approach each other, and the pointer moves from left to right over the dial. The whole mechanism is fixed in a brass case, having a hole at the back for adjusting the instrument to the mercurial barometer by means of a key, which sets the pointer without affecting the levers. The dial is generally open to show the mechanism, and is protected by a glass, to which is fitted a movable index.

This barometer is very sensitive, and has the advantage of occupying little space, although it has not yet been made as small as the aneroid. Both these instruments admit of a great variety of mounts to render them ornamental. The metallic barometer can be constructed with a small clock in its centre, so as to form a novel and beautiful drawing-room ornament.

Admiral Fitzroy writes, 'Metallic barometers, by Bourdon, have not yet been tested in very moist, hot, or cold air for a sufficient time. They are dependent, on secondary instruments, and liable to deterioration. For limited employment, when sufficiently compared, they may be very useful, especially in a few cases of electrical changes, *not foretold or shown by mercury*, which these seem to indicate remarkably.'

They are not so well adapted for travellers, nor for measurements of considerable elevations, as aneroids.

I have observed the movement of a Bourdon tube over several years on a regular basis and find that it indicates very well and is quite sensitive, normally being of a greater movement per inch of pressure than the standard aneroid of the period. This book does not cover restoration work to Bourdon barometers, although one or two are illustrated. The linkages and movements are generally of good quality, but can be time-consuming if needing repair. Some damage to bellows can occasionally be rectified. With the passage of time, the horseshoe-shaped bellows open up slightly, allowing a very small ingress of air, but with very careful manipulation and closing of these, by reshaping and then remaking the connecting levers, an operational barometer can be produced again. If the bellows have leaked, however, they are exceptionally difficult to repair without stripping right down and resoldering an evacuating tube, which is normally positioned at the top of the horseshoe-shape underneath a mountain plate. When they have leaked they frequently have microscopic holes in them and it can be very difficult to find these. Pressurising the bellows can lead to problems of stretching and damaging the tube itself. Often the metal is no longer able to withhold a vacuum. Although Bourdon barometers are collectable as individual barometers, they have not really attained a financial value worth spending many hundreds of pounds on.

Fig. 10.1 shows a Bourdon movement, removed from its case, revealing the almost circular diaphragm. When air pressure changes, the ends of the horseshoe move in and out. You can see from this movement, with the curved rack over to its furthermost extent, that the barometer is not working, the capsule having leaked air. The usual way Bourdon movements were mounted was in brass cases similar to the Dent/Vidi barometers as shown by the example in Fig. 10.2, which is a 4.5 inch dial brass-cased Bourdon metallic barometer but attributed to Richard Freres. It is a similar design of case to the Dent/Vidi barometers, the silvered dial having a wide open centre, the case with traditional hanging ring. Fig. 10.3 is of a very similar Bourdon tube barometer with large hanging ring, this time with a 4.5 inch diameter cardboard dial, front glass removed for photography. It can clearly be seen that this barometer is operational from the position of the curved brass rack.

Wooden cases were also used as can be seen in Fig. 10.4, a 7.5 inch card dial Bourdon barometer in heavy ebonised turned wooden frame, made under E. Bourdon and Richards Patent, Paris, around 1865. At the back of these types of barometer there is often a hole in the wooden case and a small turncatch which originally held the adjusting key; these are invariably missing. Carved wooden mounts were also used which reflect French taste in furniture. They were probably made in numerous styles, but comparatively few have survived. Two interesting soft metal cast cased examples are shown in Figs 10.5 and 10.6. The first has an enamelled 6 inch French dial. They often have a particular style of brass setting-hand of the open-fretted design, as can be seen

Above, Fig. 10.1: *Bourdon mechanism removed from case, showing rack assembly and curved diaphragm.*
Below left, Fig. 10.2: *A 4.5 inch engraved silvered dial Bourdon barometer in brass case, c. 1870.*
Below right, Fig. 10.3: *Bourdon barometer with 4.5 inch card dial in brass case, c. 1870.*

Fig. 10.4:
*Bourdon barometer
with 7.5 inch card dial
in heavy ebonised
wood turned case,
c. 1865.*

Fig. 10.5:
*A 6 inch enamel dial
soft metal cast
Bourdon barometer,
c. 1875.*

Fig. 10.6:
A 6 inch card dial soft metal cast Bourdon barometer, c. 1875.

here. The case of this barometer is mounted with figurines and garlands of plants. The second is another elaborately soft metal cast case, with 6 inch diameter dial Bourdon barometer mounted in, this time with a card-board dial, as is quite often found, made for the English market. Both examples prob-ably date from the period 1870–1880.

Above, Fig. 11.1: *A typical altimeter of 1920 by Short & Mason.*

Below, Fig. 11.2: *Movement from 1920 altimeter.*

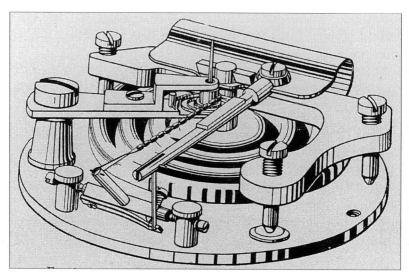

190

11 Altimeters and Surveying Aneroids

Aircraft and ballooning altimeters developed from the aneroid barometer. The altimeter measures the pressure exerted by the atmosphere and is sometimes called an aneroid, since it is very similar in construction to an aneroid barometer. However, the aneroid barometer dial is divided into inches or millimeters of mercury, but the altimeter is divided and calibrated to read height. The late Fred Pither recalled to me just before he died in 1994 how one of the jobs he had worked on when he was much younger was to make part of the barometer for the ill-fated R101. This, of course, was a mercury barometer on gimbals; so, some airships used mercury barometers but they were at a disadvantage in terms of economy of size and, presumably, weight. An aneroid altimeter has a great advantage over a mercury barometer because it is so light and compact, as well as being safe to transport. I am chiefly interested in the development of the domestic aneroid barometer, but there is a naturally close relationship with industrial and aircraft altimeter usage. Indeed, the present-day domestic aneroid barometer has almost certainly developed through the greater requirement for accuracy in instruments such as altimeters.

Fig. 11.1 shows a typical altimeter of around 1920 by Short & Mason, and Fig. 11.2 shows a good-quality aneroid mechanism of the late 1920s. The compensating steel bar can be seen on the connecting arm and the hair spring spindle mechanism is supported at an angle to the fusee chain, allowing greater movement of the arm which would, I believe, be suitable for an altimeter. The late 1920s altimeter mechanism shown in Fig. 11.3 is, to all intents and purposes, very similar to Fig. 11.2; the hair spring spindle assembly is mounted by two pillars, allowing again more movement for the fusee chain arm.

It appears that the altimeter was constantly being improved in the 1920s and 1930s. Fig. 11.4 shows the Mark 8D altimeter and mechanism which is improved in its construction by having less lag due to the pressure capsule diaphragm box having flanges soldered together (see patent no. 198838, 1922, in the Appendix). The use of the improved capsule, dating from 1922, and the U-spring mounting are probably the chief differences between normal aneroids and altimeters. After this date, there were many patents to improve altimeters by various aircraft and aviation companies – so much so that another book could be written just on the development of altimeters!

Fig. 11.5 shows a late nineteenth-century, possibly early twentieth-century, aviator's altimeter, for wearing around the wrist. Early aircraft, such as those used by the Royal Flying Corps in its very early days, were not always fitted with instrument panels, being highly crude affairs made of as lightweight a material as possible. The model illustrated is interesting in that every 500 ft division has been marked by red paint: presumably the pilot in his crude aeroplane was shaken and buffeted around so much that he was glad to see the needle divisions every 500 ft, rather than trying to focus on the finer distinctions.

Surveying aneroids are another variation of altimeters but for more precise readings as they try to measure accurately smaller variations in altitude than would normally be required for flying or ballooning altimeters. And, of course, they can also be used down mines. John Davis & Son of Derby were well known for mining instruments from Victorian days, and in their catalogues of around 1870 they advertise the Davis surveying aneroids, reading to 1 ft, priced between £6 5s and £7 7s 6d, depending on size and range of altitude readings required. Fig. 11.6 shows an extract from their catalogue of 1870. Another extract is shown in Fig. 11.7 of a colliery and engine-house aneroid barometer, which appears to be very similar to the ship's and RNLI barometers around at the time, although the faces, available in 8 inch, 10 inch, 12 inch, 15 inch and 18 inch diameters, have a silvered metal face, as opposed to the ship's barometers, which were generally porcelain or enamel.

Precision aneroids were easier to read accurately by the addition of a magnifying lens which could be moved around the edge of the barometer and could be raised and lowered to focus on the very fine

Above, Fig. 11.3: *Late 1920s altimeter movement.*

Below: Fig. 11.4: *Mark 8D altimeter in instrument housing.*

Right, Fig. 11.5: *A 2.25 inch engraved silvered dial altimeter for early aviation use, c. 1910.*

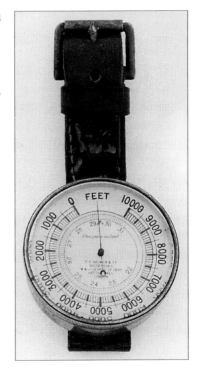

Davis's Surveying Aneroids.

Reading to One Foot.

This instrument is designed for the purpose of readily ascertaining variations, levels, &c., and from its extreme sensitiveness is found of considerable utility in mining and surveying work. Besides its extreme sensitiveness, the speciality claimed for the instrument is an arrangement of the scale of altitudes which admits of subdivision by a vernier. For mine surveying the entire circle of the dial is graduated to represent 6in. of the mercurial column—that is, from 27in. to 33in. This scale affords observations from about 2,000 feet below sea-level to 4,000 feet above. The finest division of the altitude scale (1-100th) represents 10 feet measurement, which can be again divided by the vernier scale to single feet. The vernier scale is moved by rackwork, and a lens which rotates on the outer circumference of the instrument facilitates the readings. For surface surveying purposes, where it is not required to be used below sea-level, the instrument is made with the scale divided from 25 to 31 inches, thus giving an altitude scale of 6,000 feet above sea level only, and with this open scale, and the assistance of the vernier, the readings to single feet may easily be taken. These instruments are also constructed for measuring much greater altitudes—10,000, 15,000 or 20,000 feet—but with these scales the measurement cannot be made quite so minute as in the more open scale.

The instruments are carefully compensated for temperatures.

To insure increased accuracy in surveying, two aneroids should be employed and simultaneous readings taken, one being kept at a fixed station while the surveyor is taking his readings.

It is desirable to place Aneroid Barometers, while being read, in the same position, and preferably horizontal.

Davis's Surveying Aneroid.	Price.			Cable Word.
	£	s.	d.	
3 in. Surveying Aneroid, best compensated, bronzed metal case, silvered dial, vernier moved by rackwork, reading eye-piece traversing the whole circle, altitude scale to 5000, in leather sling case... ...	6	5	0	ERO
3 in. ditto, but scale 2000 ft. below and 4000 ft. above sea-level	6	5	0	EROS
5 in. ditto, 2000 ft. below and 4000 ft. above sea-level	6	10	0	ANERO
5 in. ditto, 6000 ft. above sea-level	6	10	0	ANEROS
5 in. ditto, 15,000 ft. above sea-level... ...	7	7	6	ANEROID

Fig. 11.6:
Extract from 1870 catalogue on Davis's surveying aneroids.

needle. Fig. 11.8 is a surveying aneroid by J. Hicks of London, with 7,000 feet altitude scale and movable magnifying lens, in a brass case, inscribed on the back 'Cameroon Highlanders'. These surveying altitude barometers were, of course, also used for gunnery ranges during the First World War and no doubt other times, as air pressure and altitude have an affect on the trajectory of missiles and presumably this could be compensated for if read accurately. Fig. 11.9 shows a 4.5 inch surveying aneroid with mining scale, silvered brass dial, by Henry Pidduck & Sons of Hanley with movable magnifying lens, bronze finished case and knurled vernier adjuster to move the centre-to-centre vernier. An extremely well-made instrument of high precision and calibrated to today's National Physical Laboratory standards, it is in fact the one we have used for many years in our own pressure testing chamber. (The National Physical Laboratory

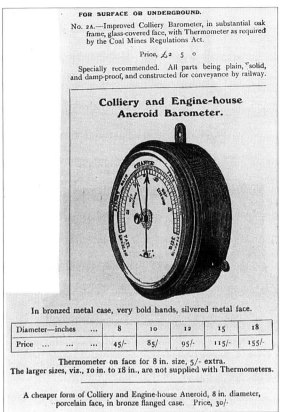

FOR SURFACE OR UNDERGROUND.

No. 2A.—Improved Colliery Barometer, in substantial oak frame, glass-covered face, with Thermometer as required by the Coal Mines Regulations Act.

Price, £2 5 0

Specially recommended. All parts being plain, solid, and damp-proof, and constructed for conveyance by railway.

Colliery and Engine-house Aneroid Barometer.

In bronzed metal case, very bold hands, silvered metal face.

Diameter—inches ...	8	10	12	15	18
Price	45/-	85/	95/-	115/-	155/-

Thermometer on face for 8 in. size, 5/- extra.
The larger sizes, viz., 10 in. to 18 in., are not supplied with Thermometers.

A cheaper form of Colliery and Engine-house Aneroid, 8 in. diameter, porcelain face, in bronze flanged case. Price, 30/-

Fig. 11.7: *Extract from 1870 catalogue on Davis's colliery and engine-house aneroid barometers.*

holds the most accurate barometer known; it is accurate to within 4/000 of a millibar and is used to calibrate scientific barometers.)

One barometer I have not been able to find an example of is the one featured in Fig. 11.10, which shows an interesting twin-needled surveying aneroid as illustrated in the F. Mildner & Co. catalogue of aneroid barometers 'A Description of the Construction and Various Uses Explained' of 1903. The small subsidiary dial indicates whether the larger hand is reading from the first circle or the second circle. I think this is quite likely to have come from patent no. 2457, dated 1889 (see Appendix) by John Thomas Daniels or at least an adaptation of the same patent. Yet another interesting barometer I have not seen is the one shown in Fig. 11.11 which is from p. 12 of a small descriptive leaflet by James J. Hicks, dated April 1900, describing Watkin's mountain aneroid with an interesting shut-off switch at the back of the case in an effort to redress the loss of reading when submitted to a diminution of pressure, particularly geared to mountaineers and

Fig. 11.8:
A 2.5 inch silvered dial surveying aneroid with magnifying lens, c. 1870.

Fig. 11.9:
A 4.5 inch silvered dial surveying aneroid with mining scale and magnifying lens, c. 1890.

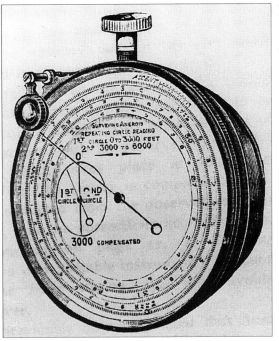

Fig. 11.10:
Twin-needle surveying aneroid, c. 1900.

Watkin Mountaineering Aneroid.

OBVERSE.   REVERSE.

PRICES.

Aluminium Barometer, divided in either French or English measure, including leather sling case.

For altitudes of 5,000 feet	...	...	£5 15 0
„ „ 10,000 „	...	...	6 2 6
„ „ 15,000 „	...	...	6 10 0
„ „ 20,000 „	...	...	6 17 6

SOLE MANUFACTURER—

J. J. HICKS,
8, 9 & 10, HATTON GARDEN, LONDON, ENGLAND.

Fig. 11.11:
Watkin mountaineering barometer from J. J. Hicks' catalogue, 1900.

Above, Fig. 11.12: *Movement of recording pocket altimeter, c. 1913.*

Below, Fig. 11.13: *Motor aneroid by Negretti & Zambra, c. 1920.*

high altitude measuring. It is particularly interesting to note that this instrument was made in aluminium, which is normally assumed to be a metal used later.

Fig. 11.12 shows the particularly fine mechanism with double diaphragm small clock of a fascinating variation from the normal barometer, being a pocket barograph, more correctly termed a pocket recording altimeter, for surveyors, travellers and explorers. They were sold by T. Cook & Sons Ltd in their 1913 catalogue. The illustration shows the mechanism with the cover removed, without a chart between the two fingers, measuring only 4.75 x 3.25 x 1.5 inches and weighing 1 lb, in a morocco-covered metal case with glass window: a very delicate instrument to be carried in the pocket, considering it had a wet ink nib pen. This very finely made mechanism is French and is one of only three I have seen. They all appear to be by the same manufacturer and design but, as there appears to be so few of them, perhaps they were not particularly popular or satisfactory. This is yet another area which needs further research, although details are difficult to find with so few catalogues surviving.

Fig. 11.13 shows a very unusual and rare item: a 2.75 inch diameter dial motor aneroid by Negretti & Zambra, number 12833, circa 1920. The outer revolving altitude scale is divided from 0 to 10,000 feet. The movement is held in a 4 inch diameter fixing plate for mounting in a vehicle.

Above, Fig. 12.1: *Free-standing brass forecaster by Negretti &*
Zambra, c. 1920.
Below left, Fig. 12.2: *Reverse of a forecaster showing easel-type*
stand (later model).
Below right, Fig. 12.3: *Reverse of a forecaster showing solid stand*
(early model).

12 Weather Forecasters

For many years I have been fascinated by the Negretti & Zambra weather forecaster. Listed in the Appendix under patent no. 6276 is the 1915 patent for this intriguing instrument. I have had many people remark how accurate it is. *The Field,* 15th February 1936, printed a report of its accuracy supplied by Ernest Heath of Cornwall which shows over 90 per cent accurate forecasts over a year. Several different designs of forecasters were made, the large brass forecaster probably being of the earlier patent and, although made continuously for many years, very few were sold. However, the small round forecaster has been extensively sold and used successfully for many years.

I have always been curious to know who Eric Wilfred Kitchin was. In 1906 he applied and was accepted to be an associate member of the Royal Meteorological Society. Then residing at The Priory, Watford, by 1915 he was living at 'Markonia' and was a civil engineer – perhaps he was involved in early radio? The only other patent I have traced to him was for a roller skate. Fig. 12.1, a brass free-standing weather forecaster by Negretti & Zambra of the 1920s, shows the original concept of Kitchin's design but in a circular case measuring 4.75 inches. As these originally sold for £2 5s, it is not surprising that few were sold when you consider that they were nine times more expensive than imitation ivory ones.

The reverse of the brass free-standing weather forecaster is illustrated in Fig. 12.2, with a flat metal easel-type frame, which I believe to be the later model, whereas Fig. 12.3 shows the reverse of an earlier brass forecaster with 'ball and socket' type easel stand, although I am uncertain of date; perhaps this one was taken out of production in the 1920s. Other styles of forecaster were made such as the imitation ivory-fronted metal desk forecaster, 5 inches high by 3 inches wide, probably sold from 1920s onwards shown in Fig. 12.4. This variation of the famous forecaster is seldom seen at auctions these days: this is only the second one I have handled. By far the

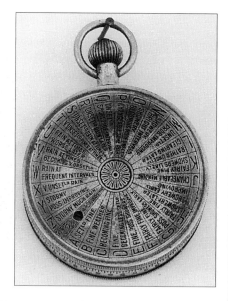

Opposite top left, Fig. 12.4: *Free-standing or wall-mountable imitation ivory deluxe forecaster, c. 1920.*

Opposite top right, Fig. 12.5: *Most common form of pocket forecaster from the 1920s to the 1950s.*

Opposite bottom left, Fig. 12.6: *A 2 inch diameter 'weather watch' with silvered dials, c. 1920.*

Opposite bottom right, Fig. 12.7: *Reverse of 'weather watch' showing the predictions.*

Fig. 12.8:
Last style of forecaster by Negretti & Zambra, c. 1970.

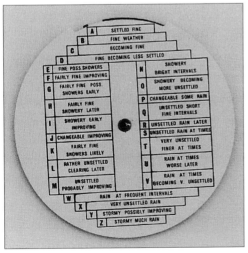

Fig. 12.9:
Reverse of Fig. 12.8.

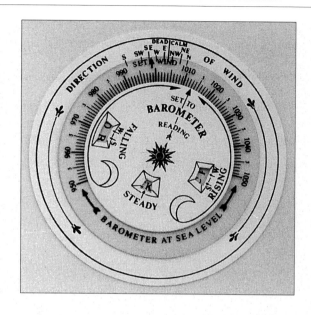

Above, Fig. 12.10: *Modern forecaster, 4.25 inch diameter in millibars.*

Below, Fig. 12.11: *Reverse of Fig. 12.10.*

Fig. 12.12: *A rare patented mahogany balance barometer by H. Mapple, c. 1860. (Sotheby's, London).*

most commonly sold forecaster was the one shown in Fig. 12.5, an imitation ivory pocket weather forecaster by Negretti & Zambra, from the 1920s onwards, which originally sold for 5s with simple printed instructions and imitation crocodile skin cardboard box. Many thousands of these were sold and they are often to be found at antique and collectors' fairs.

Barometers were also made as forecasting barometers. A very fine example is pictured in Fig. 12.6, the weather watch, the pocket weather foreteller, 2 inches in diameter, originally supplied in morocco snap case, and sold for £7 10s. This is the only one I have seen. Fig. 12.7 shows the reverse of the pocket weather foreteller, with the weather predictions. As yet, I have not come across the weather foreteller which retailed for £12 10s, a 10.5 inch diameter polished oak frame instrument, combining the brass forecaster and a barometer which can be seen in the advertising leaflets for this interesting item.

The last style of weather forecaster by Negretti & Zambra can be seen in Fig. 12.8, possibly dating from the 1970s. It has a translucent turquoise ring and measures about 2.25 inches in diameter. Interestingly, it was still produced in inches of mercury. Fig. 12.9 gives the reverse. It was sold in a simple blue plastic wallet. This curious forecaster is still available today in a modern version. Figs 12.10 and 12.11 show the front and reverse, this time in millibars, measuring approximately 4.25 inches in diameter: they are surprisingly accurate. Fig. 12.12 illustrates a very rare balance barometer patented by Henry Mapple. It has a pivoted and weighted pointer at the front with another indicator immediately behind it connected to internal gearing. The brass scale is from 27.5 to 31.5 inches, with standard weather indications, and is signed by the maker. The mahogany base is mounted on an ebonised wood stand and the height is 13.5 inches. The intrument can be protected by a glass dome.

In Henry Mapple's patent, dated 1856, no. 1029 (see Appendix), he describes in some detail a variety of balance barometers, utilising a hollow tube, thin and flexible, exhausted of air, set upon a balance of very fine design. As the air pressure changes, the weight of the hollow tube also will move and indicate on the needle at the top. Unfortunately, the hollow tube is missing in this example but it is most likely to be a corrugated conical tube, exhausted of air. A number of other designs are mentioned; the lack of surviving examples and references to this item would indicate its extreme rarity and presumably its lack of success.

Appendix: Summary of Patents

A list of patents discovered appertaining to aneroids and their development.

Date	Number	Description
1844	10157	De Fontainemoreau's specification: a new mode of constructing barometers and other pneumatic instruments.
1856	1029	Henry Mapple. Descriptive patent of various balance-type barometers, both mercury and non-mercury, utilising corrugated and evacuated tubes of various shapes.
1857	501	Photographic application on dials of graduated scales and other signs.
1857	2641	Improvements in producing graduated scales and other signs on porcelain and other ceramic and enamelled materials, for meteorological and philosophical instruments.
1858	732	Rack and pinion movement of hand from pressure box.
1862	682	Major alteration to mechanical construction of aneroid mechanism by Lucien Vidi.
1868	2119	Automatic indication whether a barometer is rising or falling.
1886	3425	Watkin patent for reading more than one revolution of a dial.
1886	14730	Watkin patent (improved) for reading more than one revolution of a dial.
1887	14424	To show pressure corrected to sea level and actual pressure at the same time.
1889	2457	Variations of pressure rendered more readily apparent and indicated with greater accuracy than can be done by single needle barometers.
1915	6276	Kitchin patent for weather forecaster.
1918	131332	Henry Hughes & Sons Ltd. Improved construction of vacuum box, pressure plate or spring, and calibrating and adjusting the system.
1922	198253	To reduce lag of instrument by use of springs.
1922	198838	Improvements in vacuum chambers and devices for aneroids (for reduction or elimination of lag in operation, change in diaphragm soldered edge).
1922	202014	To facilitate single setting of barometer to obtain direct readings simultaneously of actual atmospheric

		pressure and sea-level pressure.
1923	215844	Improvement to the mounting or location of the blade springs (introduction of U-spring to form base of movement).
1924	227312	By Goerz, to render the instrument highly insensitive to shocks, using standard aneroid boxes, irrespective of existing differences between them, while retaining the standard divisions.
1924	232510	Automatic indications in direction of change of barometer pressure.
1926	252887	Short & Mason. A more simple means of mounting and adjusting mechanism (improvements in U-shaped spring to form base of barometer).
1926	258991	Improvements in aneroid altimeters and barometers, to reduce errors of indication from angle or attitude of instrument and pointer vibration.
1927	303987	Improvement in indicating instruments.
1928	311936	W.F. Stanley & Co.: adjustment of hands for bulk head fitted barometers.
1932	407451	Short & Mason: automatic indication of barometer rising or falling.
1934	430810	Continental automatic reading of a barometer rising or falling (by electrical method).
1934	436552	Short & Mason: alteration in transmission ratio between diaphragm and needle.
1934	441190	Lufft of Germany: simultaneous reading of three instruments in one case.
1934	446651	Continental automatic indicating of rising or falling barometer.
1938	505885	Improvements to withstand vibrations for use in aircraft.
1945	588890	Object to provide a new and attractive type of aneroid barometer (the moving dial desk barometer and calendar).
1945	589005	Improvements in setting pointers for measuring instruments (spring-loaded setting knob and hand).
1945	626624	Amplifying the small mechanical movement to a comparatively greater magnitude.
1949	641127	Minister of Supply: improvements to barographs, dampening action for barographs for use on board ship.
1967	1180944	Adjustable pressure scale with respect to a separate weather scale.

Bibliography

Banfield, Edwin, *Antique Barometers: an Illustrated Survey* (Baros Books, Trowbridge, 1996).

Banfield, Edwin, *Barometers: Aneroid and Barographs* (Baros Books, Trowbridge, 1996).

Banfield, Edwin, *Barometer Makers and Retailers 1660–1900* (Baros Books, Trowbridge, 1991).

Banfield, Edwin, *The Italian Influence on English Barometers from 1780* (Baros Books, Trowbridge, 1993).

Belville, J.H., *Manual of the Mercurial and Aneroid Barometers* (London, 1849).

Bolle, Bert, *Barometers* (Antique Collectors' Club, Woodbridge, 1981).

Burnett, J. E. and Morrison-Low, A. D., *Vulgar and Mechanick: the Scientific Instrument Trade in Ireland 1650–1921* (National Museums of Scotland and Royal Dublin Society, 1989).

Clarke, T. N., Morrison-Low, A. D. and Simpson, A. D. C., *Brass and Glass* (National Museums of Scotland, 1989).

A Fellow of the Meteorological Society, *The Aneroid Barometer: How to Buy and Use It* (London, 1840).

McConnell, Anita, *Barometers* (Shire Publications, Aylesbury, 1988).

Middleton, W. E. Knowles, *The History of the Barometer* (Baros Books, Trowbridge, 1994).

Negretti & Zambra, *A Treatise on Meteorological Instruments* (Baros Books, Trowbridge, 1995).

Index